The Humor In Birth

Insight and Stories from a Doula

MICAH L. BURGESS

SixRoots Publishing

Find out more about me and my doula business at

www.wacodoula.com

This story was written for:

All the many amazing women and families who have let me into one of the most vulnerable incredible journeys of their lives! I am forever changed and grateful.

And dedicated first

to the Creator and Giver of all life,

and second, to:

my "SixRoots," Gabrielle, Jacob, Anna Joy, Isaac, Naomi and Levi. You will always have the best parts of me. I love you all and my prayer is that you will follow the dreams God has put on your hearts,

and to the man who has known me, loved me and has chosen to walk alongside me as we plant our SixRoots so that they may grow and flourish. I love you Michael and I can not imagine my life without you.

Contents

Introduction

*I*F YOU HAVE PICKED UP THIS BOOK, then you may be wondering, even doubting, how humor can be in the same sentence as birth. Most women who have given birth are willing to discuss their birth story, sharing everything from the monumental moments to the close-call complications, what they did not like and how they felt. The birth of someone's child is a BIG DEAL, and let's be honest, how these babies enter the world is "no joke!" It is hard and, at times, scary. I could write a-whole-nother book on that. I have been attending births as a doula for over the last thirty years, and my intentions have been to help normalize birth. How can I make childbirth more approachable for women while they deal with the various emotional and mental challenges it brings? Throughout this book, I share quite a few of those techniques, but my goal is to reveal a facet that maybe has been hidden from you.

There is a lyric in a song that says, "There is a joy in the journey," and, for most women, that joy tends to be your baby arriving at the end of the birth journey. Bringing joy during labor is not an easy task. We need to look for it and be conscious of the possibility that it is there. One way to experience joy is in laughter. I can definitely attest that there are some hilarious things that happen in birth. **I have found that along with the inspirational and difficult, the comical scenarios in our birth story can also be significant.** The aspect of humor being a part of someone's experience is real and worth sharing.

I was twenty years old, not married, and to be honest, getting my life back together when I attended my very first birth. My sister Maranatha's first birth was a home birth, and it felt like everyone and their dog was there. In the room were my sister and brother-in-law, the midwife, her three assistants, two close friends, my youngest sister, and me. Now, Maranatha and Matthew were some of those cool cats in the eighties who had a waterbed. I guess this situation was not ideal for giving birth because they had a blow-up mattress in the middle of their small apartment, which is probably why ten people felt like twenty. Every room was full of women; it felt like a sorority house. Some were discussing and preparing for what was ahead. Others made me feel like we were just hanging out. It was strange at first to see the lounging, the eating, the sleeping. But somewhere along the way, the experience of my sister's childbirth felt normal and comfortable. No one was fretting over my sister, and everyone was just carrying on like business as usual. Even my brother-in-law was acting normally.

Something you should know about my brother-in-law is that he is a neat freak! He washes the dishes as soon as the last person takes his or her last bite. The clothes in his drawers are neatly placed in their exact spot. (I know this because one day I borrowed a pair of his running shorts and quickly returned them before he even knew they were gone. Well, he did know and asked me about it because they were not in their exact place. Foolishly, I lied, and he has teased me mercilessly ever since.) Even the change on his dresser is organized by greatest to smallest. I have never seen their place messy, and I know this is all Matthew because my sister was a slob growing up.

Naturally, while waiting for the birth, he spent a lot of his time following behind all the women, picking up after them. He straightened up and wiped off so much that, at times, my sister would have to call his name to come back to be with her. At one point, Matthew was holding her hand, and during a very hard contraction, a spill occurred. The commotion was a little distracting, and you could hear someone asking about paper towels. I could see Matthew looking anxiously around, desperately wanting to help.

He was about to get up when my sister squeezed his hand and, during her contraction, wailed, "They're in the second cabinet to the right under the microwave behind the extra Mr. Clean sponges!" *LOVE IT!*

As labor continued, I watched my sister walk and sway slowly throughout the house. She would rock in her rocking chair or sometimes lie down.

She would go outside for a few minutes, then wobble to the kitchen for a snack. Every time I looked up, she seemed to be somewhere different.

We need a golf commentator.

"Okay folks, I think we've spotted her. Yes, Maranatha Chapman is in the living room leaning up against the wall and... wait, now she's making her way to the potty. Check that, she's on her side lying on the couch and, now folks, she has made her way back to the bedroom on her hands and knees. We will keep you updated as we get more information. Back to you, Ted."

The way she was acting reminded me of that time our cat gave birth; uncomfortable and desperately trying to get away from it all. Somehow, she finally landed in the tub; Maranatha, not the cat. It was a peaceful time for her. The room was lit by candles, music was playing, and everyone had left the room except for me and my two sisters. It was perfect. My younger sister and I talked and encouraged Maranatha through each contraction.

"Great job, breathe."

Like I know anything.

Everything was going smoothly and then during one contraction she sounded like she was struggling to breath.

"It's okay, just breathe."

She became more restless. Amelia and I tried to comfort and reassure her.

"Breathe, Mara. You're doing fine. Keep breathing."

She looked desperate and began moving around quite a bit. In my mind I knew this was it; she has hit that part people talk about.

"Don't panic. Everything's okay. Don't forget to breathe."

Okay, now I'm starting to sound like Thor in the movie Ragnarok where he's trying to keep Bruce Banner from turning into The Hulk. "Hey big guy, sun's getting low. Shhhh. Sun's getting real low. Shhhhh. Sun's going down..." Shut up already!

"Maranatha, it's okay, just brrree..."

Finally, through a gasp for air, she pointed at my sister. "Your shorts are on fire!"

"WHAT?!"

I looked over at my sister who had been leaning against the wall by the tub and, sure enough, the edge of her shorts had caught fire from one of the candles! We scrambled, frantically splashing water on her. The floor, the wall, my sister were all soaked, but we managed to put the flame out.

We glanced at each other; a roar of laughter filled the room. Maranatha let out a wail mid-laugh. *Oh yeah, we're havin' a baby in here!*

My sister's birth experience had so much significance for me beyond just the entertaining aspects. I saw how amazing our bodies work and decided to have natural births myself. This experience also helped to shape my career path in becoming a doula. Most importantly, my nephew's birth was like my own rebirth. I had strayed from God and family for the past two years. Coming home and being a part of this miracle stirred my heart and actually helped me find myself. To this day, my nephew Benjamin and I share a special bond. I have shared with him the significance of his "birth-day" in my life. More times than not on his birthday he will send me a message or call acknowledging the special day that we share. To me, birth is spiritual, empowering, and positive. I try to bring each one of those attributes to every birth I attend.

Each birth has its own special feel, its own character. Every woman's story is significant and important. This book does not take away from the miracle of birth. It is not meant to lessen anyone's pain from trauma or loss. I am not suggesting that every birth is funny. Some are serious from the word "go." What I am hoping to do is to shine a spotlight on an aspect of birth that is rarely talked about. The humor, the enjoyment, the giggles, the jokes, the amusement, the candor, and the lighthearted parts of childbirth can be powerful. This part of birth reminds the laboring mom that she is okay. When the atmosphere in the room feels heavy and daunting, a little humor can strengthen her mentally and assist her in getting to the end.

This book is my attempt to show that joy and fun can be a part of making your birth experience positive. It is okay for us to laugh at ourselves! It is actually quite healing. Come on this journey with me to a side of childbirth that you may have never experienced before.

Micah Burgess
Waco, Texas
#doitwithadoula

it's personal

*B*EFORE I START SHARING anyone else's birth stories, I want to give you a window into the humorous and entertaining parts of my six births from labor to delivery to recovery.

Labor

Before we begin, let's be clear about what "labor" really is. When I say labor, I am referring to the part of birth where you are waiting for progress and change to happen so that you can push and deliver your baby. The cervical opening enlarges from zero to ten centimeters and completely thins out. This process takes time and, for many women, is the hardest part of childbirth.

Looking back, I really was blessed to have had truly great labor experiences. My labors lasted anywhere from three to five hours. I stayed relaxed and was in control. Don't hate me, y'all. At my second birth (Jacob), I was playing bridge with my husband, my mom, and stepdad when contractions began. I would stop during the contractions, breathe through them, then go right back to the action. My sisters doubted that I was even in labor. I was on a winning streak and played cards until I was nine centimeters. There was no way I was conceding anything, that included labor. It's all a competition in my family! For my fourth birth (Isaac), I did not want to call my midwife because I just was not convinced that I was in labor. It took my very good, strong-willed friend to insist that she be called. Thank goodness I did because my midwife almost missed the birth!

For whatever reason, I just intuitively understood labor and what I needed to do. **My birth experiences are for sure a contributing factor into my journey of becoming a doula.** I had friends and family asking me to attend their births so that I could help them achieve the same type of positive experiences. I am so thankful for this.

Now delivery, that is a-whole-nother story.

Delivery

My first five births were home births. For each birth, when it came time to push, that is when all the entertainment began. Now, I'm not saying that I was necessarily laughing at the time. Remember, I was the one doing all the work and feeling all the discomfort of childbirth. However, at each birth, I could feel the smiles and lightheartedness of those who were there with me, and I drew strength from knowing that in that moment, everything was okay. **The humor that filled the room reminded me that birth is normal, I am normal.** I was surrounded by people who cared about me and who were enjoying this experience with me. It allowed me to do the same.

At my first birth (Gabrielle), I was sitting on the birthing stool, pushing, when my midwife tried to engage with me.

"Micah, that's Baby. Want to feel Baby's head?"

Everything was happening so fast and was getting harder by the second. I could not really focus on what to do, much less what I wanted.

With an irritated, panicked voice I responded, "Not. Right. NOW!"

I'm workin' over here, lady... where you been?

At that moment, my husband reached around me (I was leaning up against him) and touched her head. He immediately started to cry. I let out a big sigh as I waited for him to recover.

We got no time for tears, yo... trying to have a freakin' baby. Have y'all lost your ever-lovin' minds?

Baby was coming fast, and I could not wrap my head around what I was about to do. I felt small and scared. Those contractions were not waiting on me, though. They were coming every minute, and I was not recovering well between them. I was getting out of breath, but my midwife kept asking if I wanted to touch Baby's head. She grabbed my hand at one point and tried to get me to touch her. I jerked it back immediately.

I can't focus on a baby right now; I'm trying to have a freakin' baby!

Another contraction began and the midwife and her team let out a "WHOOAA!" as they fell backwards. They had been kneeling in front of me and my water broke. It was like the splash zone at the water park; they were soaked! I felt no remorse.

Ha! Serves you right for bothering me while I'm clearly trying to have a freakin' baby, people!

"HUUUUUUUUUUUH! MMMMMMMMMMMMAAAAAAAAA!"

"That's great, Micah! Do that again!"

"HUUUUUUUAAAAAAAAA! OW, OW, OW, OOOOOOOOUCHIIIIE! YOU GUYS!"

"That's baby's head, Micah. Keep goin'."

"Push, babe. You can do it. Let's see this sweet baby." More tears, smiles, and support from this man I love.

"AAAAAAAAAAAAAAAAAAAAAH! WHAT'S HAAAAPPENNING?!"

"Baby's here, Micah!"

"You did it, babe! I'm so proud of you!"

"Wait, WHAT?!"

I felt like I was on another planet. Where did this thing come from that was now in my arms?

Oh yeah, I just had a freakin' baby!

Sometimes the very easy and the very obvious are not always so easy or obvious to the laboring mom. At my third birth (Anna Joy), my midwife would ask a very simple question, and you would have thought that she had just asked me if I wanted to climb Mount Everest while singing "She'll Be Comin' 'Round the Mountain" at the top of my lungs.

"Micah, I can feel Baby's head.

Don't you dare ask me if I can feel baby's head!

She's almost here, but the water bag is in the way. Want me to go ahead and break your water so you can be done sooner rather than later?"

Are you crazy? Why are you talking to me? What are you trying to do to me?

"Wait? WHAT?! I'm already at my limit, Toni!"

My sister, who was with me in the room, chimed in quickly knowing my look and tone meant I was not ready to take on such colossal feats.

"Micah, it doesn't hurt to break your water. You won't feel anything. Baby will just come on down, then you'll give just a couple of pushes, and she'll be here."

The midwife spoke up. "Oh, sorry, Micah. I didn't know you thought it would hurt."

Yep. You're gonna have to spell it ALL out for me. Remember, I'm in the middle of pushing out a CANTALOUPE!

"Okay, I guess? I'm just feeling unsure and exhausted."

"Alright, Micah. You ready to push?"

"Wait? You did it already?"

"Oh yeah, no problem at all. Her head is already crowning."

See, simple.

With my fifth baby (Naomi), I was enormous! Toni had already let me know that this baby was going to be bigger than all my others. For her to say this to me was pretty significant because my first four were all around nine pounds each.

You mean, I'm giving birth to a baby elephant!?

It was time to give birth, and I was in my bathtub going through transition and hurting. I began thinking about when my oldest daughter and I went to lunch together a few weeks prior. When we finished eating and got up to leave, I took a few steps and was in agony! This giant baby was doing a number on my body. My hips, my pelvis, my pubic bone, my tailbone were all screaming at me. I stopped to gather myself, then proceeded to take a few more steps out of the restaurant. I stopped again and started to cry as I looked at my sweet daughter.

"Honey, I can't take another step. You're gonna have to call your dad to come and pick us up."

She looked at me with a quizzical face. Our car was parked just a few rows down. She glanced at the car and started to say something, but then thought better of it. She called her daddy as instructed and explained the situation. She paused for his response and then gave two answers, "Yep," and "I'm sure." Twenty minutes later, my hero showed up and helped me into the front seat of his car.

My thoughts returned, and I was back in the tub in labor. I was getting nervous about delivering my, potentially, biggest baby yet. I began to imagine how delivery was going to feel if she had already given me that much pain a few weeks ago.

The same wonderful midwife, Toni, who delivered my last two babies, was asking me another seemingly non-threatening question.

"Micah, you're doing so good, and the tub seems to be helping a lot. What do you think about staying in the tub and delivering in here?"

Again with the questions! Why are you torturing me?

"I don't know. We haven't talked about a water birth." Cue contraction. I bolted up out of the water. "Get me out of here. She's coming!"

Getting me out of that tub was no small task. The walls on that tub were very high and it took six out of the nine people in attendance to lift me out while having a contraction. One of my friends that was assisting in this job announced that she just could not look at my "nekkid" body (In Texas we are "nekkid," not naked.) So, she closed her eyes while she helped my-"buck-nekkid"-self onto dry land.

Hello? Excuse me? Open your eyes, woman!

We headed to the birthing stool **(if possible, this should be every woman's go-to delivery**

spot!), and I began yelling to anyone that would listen.

"Get me something to put on!" *Really? This is what I'm worrying about?*

It took five of the nine people in the room to get me my sleep shirt. I am so glad I had an entourage that day. It takes a village, you know. I got settled and started receiving some coaching on how to relax and wait for another contraction to come. Nope.

"HUUUUUUUUUUUUH!"

I felt a sudden urge and began pushing. I bore down a little longer, then her head was born. I was not prepared for what was next.

I started screaming. "GET HER OUT! GET HER OUT NOW, TONI!"

"Micah, you are gonna have to push her out."

Now, if you have already given birth before you know that once the head is born then the hard part is over. The baby's body usually just slips on out with a very simple push. Unless your baby is already child-size and her shoulders are stuck.

"WHAT? I ALREADY DID!"

My amazing husband, who thinks I am Superwoman (Ladies, this can be a good thing or a bad thing), spoke up. "Honey, you've got this. You're gonna have to push again. Come on now, you can do this."

I drew in a mighty breath. "GET HER OUT, GET HER OUT, GET HER OUT!" I sounded like the "William Tell Overture" minus the stampede of horses.

Get 'er out, Get 'er out, Get 'er OUT, OUT, OUT! Get 'er out, Get 'er out, Get 'er OUT, OUT, OUT! Get 'er out, Get 'er out, Get 'er OUT, OUT, OUT! Get 'er OOOOOOOUT... GET HER OUT, OUT, OUT!

Finally, Baby was born! I felt relief, but then heard nothing. No one was making a sound. I looked around at everyone in the room and their faces were in disbelief. I was really confused and thought something might be wrong.

My midwife broke the silence with a quick word of action. "Let's get Micah on the bed."

Somebody tell me what's going on!

I could not speak because I was exhausted and hurting.

I looked at Michael and, with a reassuring smile, he said, "You did it, babe! She's here. I'm so proud of you."

"Is everything okay?"

"Yep, you're bleeding a little more than Toni would like, so she's having you rest. She's getting some medicine for you to take to help with the bleeding."

"What about the baby? Is she okay? Where is she?"

"They're cleaning her up for you, and she's great!"

Then I heard lots of chatter and giggles and one of my friends say, "Alright, I'm takin' bets. Everybody give your best guess."

I heard shouts of numbers and laughter. Finally, one response stuck out and I realized what was being said.

"I think she's ten pounds!"

Are you kidding me?

My face went white, and Michael looked at me with a mischievous grin.

"You are one strong woman!"

My sister piped up. "She's huge, Micah! We gotta weigh her right now! I can't stand it!"

It was fine with me. I was too tired to have an opinion about anything at that moment. The crowd assembled near the baby and scale. It took four of the nine people in the room to get her there. I could not see her very well, so I truly had no idea what she weighed. My lady parts were telling me that I did not just push out a cantaloupe, I birthed two watermelons!

It was the moment of truth; she was on the scale, her weight about to be announced.

"None of you are right," the midwife assistant shouted. She removed her hand that was covering up the amount and gasps filled the room.

I still could not see anything.

"What? What is it?"

Once again, my sister belted out, "SHE'S TWELVE POUNDS, MICAH! WHAT THE HECK?!"

I winced when she said the number. *That's just too big!* I sat bewildered as they brought this "baby" over to me.

"Now, Micah, she's actually too heavy for you to hold right now without assistance. So, let Michael help you out."

My husband was a biology major and excellent with facts and knowledge. You could tell he was questioning their findings.

"That can't be right. How can she be twelve pounds?"

Toni handed the baby to Michael and, while trying not to drop her, he exclaimed, "Oh, good grief! She's a hoss!"

Well, isn't that endearing?

I took one look at this sweet baby girl, and, as Michael helped me hold her, had an epiphany. *I have no clothes for this child.*

I will end this part by telling you that my sister had to go out the next day and purchase three-month-old clothes for my chunky monkey.

Recovery

So those were my great labors and eventful deliveries. My responses and recoveries were also all different with each birth.

My first birth (Gabrielle) was a very traumatic recovery because I had a hematoma inside my labia. *Yes, it is as bad as it sounds!* I was in bed for almost two weeks. Every time I would get up, I would feel faint. It was so swollen, and it hurt so much. I made the mistake one time of using a mirror. *You see where this is going?* I held the mirror down low where all the pain was, and y'all, I was swollen from the inside OUT! You could not even tell I was a female! To this day, I cannot hear the word "HE-MA-TO-MA" without cringing and gagging. Enough of that, moving on.

After the birth of my second child (Jacob), I went shopping the day after he was born. Let it be known that this is not the wisest thing to do, but, to my point, I felt ten million times better than the first time around!

After my third birth (Anna Joy), I fell asleep. The midwife had the baby laying on the bed right beside me while she did all the newborn tests. She was crying, and I was snoring. *Don't mind me. I'll be over here sleeping. Y'all got this.*

With my fourth (Isaac), as soon as he was born, I had someone make me Chinese food. I was starving!

As mentioned earlier, with my fifth (Naomi), I was wrapping my head around the fact that I needed help holding this twelve pound "baby" who had no clothes to wear.

The most monumental recovery would have to be with my sixth baby (Levi). Pretty much everything surrounding his birth was challenging and scary. I had to have an emergency Cesarean because he was born at twenty-seven weeks, only 2.1 pounds. I had to go under anesthesia, and my incision was not the bikini friendly kind. It was faster to go old school: vertical. *Okay Micah, where's the humor?*

While I was in recovery, Michael was with the baby. Two of my closest friends were in the room when I woke up, and I was still feeling loopy. Apparently, I started talking about having to be shaved for the surgery.

"Hey, y'all, I got a Brazilian Bikini Wax."

At that moment, I proudly pulled up my gown to show off my "spa-day" at the hospital. They laughed, then one of them started talking about her last experience with waxing.

"I didn't like how my last Brazilian looked. I think I'm gonna try having all the hair removed. It's called a "newborn."

I listened, considered, then added my two cents. "A newborn? Hmmmm? No thanks. I don't want to look like an eight-year-old!"

More laughter erupted. Gotta love the uncensored comments that come with anesthesia. I think childbirth is one of the few times that "no filter" is acceptable.

Even with my micro-preemie, it has been important to me to find those places where I can smile and even laugh. The truth is my last birth is our little miracle baby. It was touch and go for about an hour after Levi was born.

I am pleased to tell you that Levi was released from the NICU a month before expected; absolutely nothing wrong with my boy! We give God all the glory on this one!

Okay! Y'all ready to be entertained? Now, take a really good deep breath. That's good, and hold it… five, four, three… you got it, two, one, and… Let's do this!

CHAPTER 2

amateur vs. veteran

*T*HROUGHOUT THIS BOOK YOU will read stories from first-time newbies to birthing pros and their responses to birth when it comes to preparation. There is a clear advantage that moms with multiple birth experiences have when it comes to making choices about their birth experience. It is the approach that we take on making decisions; you get more confident the more times you do it. Here is an example of what I am talking about.

I had a client that was going to try to deliver via VBAC (vaginal birth after Cesarean), but Baby was breech. As the time for delivery was nearing and Baby was not turning on his own, my client began to rethink her plan. We had multiple conversations throughout her pregnancy, and she finally told me that she simply did not feel peaceful anymore about trying for a vaginal delivery. Listen, I do not question a woman when she says she has prayed and thought long and hard about an important decision. This is not my birth, my baby, or my life. You have to live with your choices. Be confident and pay attention to what seems good for you and your family. Parenting is hard and it starts at pregnancy. **Trust your instincts and do not let doubt shame you.**

So, my client opted for a planned C-section on her due date. I arrived at the hospital that morning to give some emotional support; after all, I was still her doula. Both my client and her husband seemed peaceful about their decision. I waited in their hospital room for about thirty minutes, then the nurse came to take me to the recovery room. When I arrived, Baby was in the warmer, and Dad was looking at him while we waited for my client to return. The baby was semi-wrapped up in a blanket, and I asked the Dad if he wanted to hold his little boy. He seemed hesitant to pick him up, but he did want to take a look at him.

We pulled the blanket away from the baby, and instead of it being extended down next to the other, one of his little legs was folded up by his chest. He was snuggling his foot! We both gasped and laughed. The nurse came back in to put a new diaper on the baby. Nope. This baby had his eyes closed and looked quite comfy. Every time she pulled his leg down, it popped right back up against his body!

We gazed at this little one who could not straighten his leg out or hold it down. It then became a little game where we would push his leg down, and he would pop it back up. We did this over and over. We even tried to swaddle him. He was not having it. He finally grabbed his foot and held on for dear life.

Okay, little man, you win the Contortionist Award!

Did y'all catch it? This mama's instincts were right on. That baby was absolutely folded in half in utero and was "presenting" bottom, not head. Trying for a regular vaginal delivery would have been very dangerous and a VBAC even more so. She went with her gut and trusted her God. **Every**

first-time mom, every first-time dad, if paying attention, will discover how they want to navigate this parenting thing. And yes, it starts at birth.

One of the most drastic differences between amateurs and veterans is deciding when it is time to go to the hospital. **So, you think you are in labor?** Are you reading all the signs and symptoms to determine whether or not this is the real deal? Is it time to head to the hospital or birthing clinic? Should you have your midwife go ahead and come to your house? I am usually one of the first people a mama calls when she thinks she is in labor. This means that for first-time moms, upon the very FIRST sign of labor, I am being alerted.

Here is what I tell my clients: **"Ignore it."** Yep, you heard me. Distract yourself. Do your day. **Put the binoculars down!** The more you focus on early labor, the longer your birth will seem. Think about it: at home, you can do just about anything you want. You can take a walk around the block instead of in a circle in front of the monitors. You can take a nap in your own bed instead of a hospital bed hooked up to everything known to man. You can eat actual food as opposed to kindergarten snacks like popsicles, graham crackers, and Jell-O. You even have the option of getting into a bath. Normalcy is your friend. It keeps you feeling like a human for a longer period of time. Very soon, the "put together" will disappear, and the primal will take over. **Pay no attention until your attention can be nowhere else.**

First-timers, God bless 'em, can be slightly obsessive when it comes to analyzing signs of labor. Every pee color, vaginal tingling, cramp, or gas pain is scrutinized. The truth is, they are just ready to have their baby, and the hope is that they are one step closer. To a first-time mom, everything means, "I am in labor."

"Yes, cleaning out your garage could be a sign of nesting but it's not a guarantee that today's the day."

"I see, you're feeling nauseous and tired? Maybe try taking a nap first before heading into the hospital right away."

"You're cramping but have no pain? That's a great indication that your body is warming up. It's still too early to say whether or not you should call your parents to fly in from Hawaii."

"Yep, losing your mucus plug definitely indicates sometime soon." *Thanks for the pic.*

Don't get me wrong. I actually like the play-by-play of everything that is happening to them because it tells a story. The sooner I can get an overall picture of how my client is progressing, the better I can help them plan. I just have to smile a little because the sweet first-time mamas do not know what they are in for.

Soon, you won't be wondering if labor has started; you'll be wondering when it's going to end.

One question I get asked a lot from these pregnant mamas is what they can do to get labor started in the first place. They are way past being done. There are several options like special oils and herbs, walking, eating pineapple, and getting in some water, that can help your body get ready for labor. However, none of these things start labor. "What about castor oil?" NO! Just NO! All that is really going to do is give you cramps that do not lead to contractions; they lead to diarrhea. The truth is, nothing you can do will produce the outcome you are looking for except for actually delivering the baby.

I do, however, have my go-to tip for toning the uterus and softening your cervix: sex. You heard me, SEX! When a frantic client looking for advice calls because she is thirty-nine weeks, one centimeter dilated, and fifty percent effaced, I give plenty of recommendations to help her prepare her body. Then, I remind her that intercourse is the best course of action to get the job done. Yes, you have to be a little more creative because that belly is in the way. I know, it is too much work and you are too tired. I did not say the goal was pleasure... for you, anyway. One client's husband texted me back with a response to my suggestion.

"You are worth every penny! We have had sex maybe three times since she found out she was pregnant until she talked with you. Thank you, thank you, THANK YOU!"

You're welcome. Now go pick up her favorite meal, and while you are at it, put gas in her car. After dinner, draw her a bath, then go wash some dishes. (I don't know about you, but in our house, my husband washing dishes is foreplay.) And remember, start the romance earlier in the evening, bro. Pregnant women are toast after eight-thirty.

What about these pros? I have had many repeat clients over the years, as well as other women who hire me for their second or third birth. Talk about calm, confident, and sometimes, flippant women.

Veterans be like, "Hey girl, been having some contraction-like tightening for the past several hours. They're about three to four minutes apart but they're just not as strong as with my first birth. I'm gonna take a quick shower, grab a bite, and drop the kids off at my mom's. Figured I could head to the hospital after that just to see what's goin' on."

"Sorry for the late text (2:00 a.m.), but I was having some contractions while we were out to dinner. On the way home my water broke. I decided to get some sleep and I just woke up to lots of very strong contractions right on top of each other. Danny thinks we should go in, but I'd like to sleep a little bit longer. Any thoughts?"

Yep, it doesn't sound like Baby is gonna let you catch any more ZZZ's.

Or the husband calls me: "Hey Micah, this is Chad. (moaning in the background) Phoebe can't decide if she should go in yet or not. I thought I should call you."

Laboring mom in the background: "Tell Micah I'm feeling lots of pressure, but it's too soon for that. Oooooaaaaah!"

"Did you catch that Micah?"

UMMMM, yep! Y'all are having a home birth.

Trying to decide whether it is time to head to the hospital or call the midwife is not quite as obvious as we would like it to be. It would be great if, when you were in active labor and about to be pushing soon, the ambient temperature in the room stayed at a perfect seventy degrees, your body released a beautiful aroma of Jasmine flowers, all body hair disappeared, a third arm grew from your hip to apply the perfect amount of pressure on your back, and suddenly you could hear your baby's heartbeat. Wouldn't that be great?

It all boils down to this. **If you are a first-time mom and you are not sure if you are in labor, then you are probably not. If you are a pro and you are not quite convinced you are in labor, run to the car!**

CHAPTER 3

the greatest fear

*W*HAT IS A WOMAN'S greatest fear as she heads into childbirth? Is it the hours she will be in labor? Is it the "ring of fire"? How about tearing? All of these are of great concern to women, no doubt. But the greatest fear of all is the thought that while pushing, you might poop. Yep, that's the greatest fear. The absolute horror of pooping while you are pushing! Oh, the shame!

Let me set the record straight: You ARE going to poop when you deliver. I mean, it is just a fact. And before you say that you did not poop at your birth; they lied. SAY WHAT?! Now, stay with me for a second. Unless you completely emptied your bowels before you got to the hospital and pooped again on the potty right before you started pushing, it is inevitable.

Think about it. The vagina and the rectum are beside each other inside a woman's body. When pregnant, the uterus contains your baby with an average size head that is about twelve to fourteen inches around. Ever pooped anything that big? The baby grows inside the uterus which pushes up against the rectum. As that head is coming down during birth, it is "scraping" alongside the rectum. If something is in the way, it has got to come out!

While it is many women's worst fear, pooping actually means you are pushing in the right place and that Baby's head is coming down. That is why when a woman says, "I feel like I need to poop," I and all the nurses throw a party. *You are all in now, girlfriend!*

Trying to convince a laboring mama, however, that pooping during delivery is normal, is like telling her it is normal to give birth upside down. She's just not buyin' what you're sellin'. Take Beatrice for example.

"Oh my goodness, I feel like I need to poop."

"That's great, girl. That pressure is probably Baby's head comin' down."

"Uhhhh, nope. I need to poop right now." Beatrice jumped out of the bed and practically ran to the bathroom. "Move, move, move! I don't want to poop on this floor."

I am always in the habit of alerting a nurse when a woman says she needs to poop. I have no idea if she has another thirty minutes of pushing, or if Baby's head is crowning. I have a hard, fast rule: **I DO NOT DELIVER BABIES!**

In came the nurse. "Hey, Beatrice. Micah said you're feelin' some pressure?"

"No. I'm not feeling pressure... I need to poop, y'all!"

"Well, how 'bout I check you real quick to make sure it's not just Baby's head you're feeling."

"Absolutely not! I do not want to poop on you!"

The nurse and I tried to convince Beatrice that we were not worried about her pooping. In fact, we wanted to see her poop. Wait, hold up. We do not WANT to see your feces. We just like it when there is poop. Ok, we still sound gross. Nevertheless, when there is poop, a head is close behind.

"Beatrice, look at me for just a second." I attempted to calm her down so that she would relax and let this process take place. Beatrice stopped and looked at me with terror in her eyes. "You do not want to have your baby on the potty or the bathroom floor, right? The nurse will know right away if Baby's head is here or if you really just need to empty your bowels. There is nothing to be afraid of. We're right here, and you're doing great!"

Beatrice agreed and climbed back into the bed. The nurse grabbed a glove and did a quick check.

"Yep. Baby is right here, Beatrice. It's time to start pushing."

"Wait? What!? No, no, no. It's not time to start pushing. I don't think I can do this."

Now here is what is puzzling to me about a woman giving birth who FINALLY gets to this stage of the game. This is the moment you have been working towards! This is what you have been waiting for! You are here. You are almost done. What do you mean, "no, no, no"?

"I can't, Micah. I'm afraid I'm gonna poop!"

Okay, y'all. Here was my solution to this problem. Get ready.

"I totally understand that. But you know what, we know now that it's Baby's head. I don't think you're gonna have to worry about pooping. Let's just try to bear down a little with this next contraction, give me a little push, and we'll see what happens."

"Okay. I'm starting one right now. MMMUUUUUUH! HUUUUUUUUUUAAAAH! SOOOMETHING IIIS HAAAPPENING!"

"That's it, Beatrice! You're doing it! Keep goin', girl. We can see Baby's head."

Not another word was mentioned about poop because with one more big push, Baby was born... And so were a couple of little pellets. SHHHHHHH.

Not all of my clients are that easily distracted from what causes them so much stress. Let's take Hope for example. She decided to have a home birth, and her husband, Allan, was extremely supportive and very involved. I absolutely loved working with him! Labor had been going really well but transition had not. She seemed to be stuck at nine centimeters because Baby's head was not lined up well. Allan had been sitting behind her up on the bed, and she was leaning back on him. I had her angle her body a little bit so she was lying on her side. She shifted to her hip, and a contraction started. Then, all of a sudden...

"OH MY GOD! I'M ABOUT TO POOP!"

"It's okay, Hope. That's actually really good. That means Baby probably turned, and you're gonna be pushing soon."

"OOOOOOH NOOOOOOO! AHHHHHHH! ALLAN! ALLAN!"

"I'm right here, babe! You got this!"

"GEET UP! HMMMMMMUH! HUUURRY!"

Allan did not move as we waited for the contraction to end.

"I'm going to poop on you! GET UP!"

"Hope, listen, it's okay. You're not gonna poop on Allan."

"How do you know? I'm sitting on him!"

"No babe. I'm behind you. You're not sitting on me. It's gonna be okay."

Cue contraction.

"OOH, OOH, OOH, OOH, UP, UP, UP, GET UP!"

Hope soon began trying to get herself up from her position while contracting and trying not to push.

"Hope. It's okay. You need to take a deep breath and relax. Sink into that contraction."

"E-E-E-E-E! MAKE! IT! STOP! I CAN'T PUSH!"

Okay, y'all, this mama was refusing to push because she was so terrified of pooping that her contraction was starting to come down.

Now's my chance to refocus this mama.

"Hope. I know you're upset and concerned. You're gonna have to give in to the process. That pressure and urge to push is a good thing."

"I am gonna CRAP all over my husband!"

I give up.

"Okay, Allan, let's get you out of there."

We helped Hope to sit up a little so that Allan could scoot out of the way.

"You ready for the next contraction?"

"What am I supposed to do?"

"Go towards that pressure that you're feeling in your bottom."

"You mean poop?!"

"Girl, if that's what it's gonna take to have this baby, isn't it worth it?"

"I just really don't want to poop."

Yeah, caught that. Once again, watch the magic.

"Okay, Hope. No problem. If you don't want to poop, then you can just breathe through these contractions. Maybe you'll be able to successfully get away from that feeling. You just let us know when you're ready to have this baby."

"Here comes another, you guys. OOOOOOHHHHHHH! E-E-E-E-E-UUUUUUUH! NO, NO, NO! HUUUUMMMMMMAAAH!"

How's that workin' for ya?

"AM I POOPING?!"

"HUUUUUUUUUUUUUUUUH!"

"Nope. That's Baby's head. Keep going, Hope." Yep, you guessed it. I lied.

There was one time a client was in the middle of pushing, and she said, "What's that smell? AM I POOPING?!"

"I don't think so. Maybe someone just has a little gas."

"NO. I smell poop!"

"HUUUUUUUUUUUUUAAAAAAAAAAH! I'M POOOOOOPING!"

"No girl, that's just... OH, Heeeeeeey, here comes Baby!"

I thought I dodged that bullet; however, the first thing out of her mouth after Baby was born was, "Y'all, seriously. Did I poop?"

"Nope."

'Nuff said.

Now don't judge me just yet. This is the only time I lie to my clients. It is for their own good, as you can see. So here is my public apology to all of my former clients. **Yes, you pooped, and I lied. Sorry, friend.** I know, it is the end of the world as you know it.

You gonna be okay? Of course you are. Atta girl.

And finally, we have Tish. This story is a little different because Tish already had her baby. She did a fabulous job, by the way. While in recovery, the nurse was taking vitals and asking her a few questions. She handed Tish two tablets to take and told her it was so she would not get constipated (that can be a real bummer to your already-sore bottom). No one wants to push anything out down there for quite some time after delivering a baby, much less get impacted with very hard stools. *Misery.* Tish took the tablets with no dispute. The nurse continued with her tasks of cleaning Tish up, then left the room.

After about five minutes, Tish looked over at me and her eyes widened. Panic swept across her face. "Micah, I need to get to the bathroom. This stool softener is kicking in quick."

Hmmmmm. That seems fast.

"You bet. Hold onto my arm, and I'll help swing your leg over towards me."

Before Tish could even grab my arm, she put her hands down on the bed and lifted her bottom up. Brown water came pouring out!

"What the hell?"

"Oh my gosh, Tish. Are you okay?"

I buzzed the nurse, and a voice over the intercom asked how she could help.

Tish answered. "Uh, yeah! I'm sitting in liquid poop! Please hurry!"

I began helping Tish get out of the bed. I'm telling you, there was no great option here. We managed to get her leg over to my side of the bed, and she got one foot on the ground. She began to stand, then, GUSH!

"HOLY SHIT!"

I smirked, then chuckled. "Literally, my friend!"

Tish burst into a loud roar of laughter!

Phew, that could have gone either way.

We were both so amused that we were not making much ground getting to the toilet.

"Oh my gosh, Micah! What's wrong with me?"

"I seriously have NO idea! I have never seen this before."

Tish and I began taking steps towards the bathroom.

"Well, it's still comin'." Pooped dripped down Tish's legs. "And there's some more. Have fun with that, gang."

We were now screaming with laughter, that I almost peed my pants! I was about to join her in this liquid frenzy. With every step she took, squirt, squish, splash. She was in rare form.

"I hope they're bringing a cleaning crew."

I can't. I'm done.

I have never laughed so hard as a doula, but Tish took the experience like a champ. By the way, she ended up making a formal complaint to the hospital because we found out that the nurse not only gave Tish the stool softener too soon, but she was only supposed to give her ONE tablet. *Ay, ay, ay, Lucy, you got some splainin' to do!*

Every woman in childbirth should take a page out of Tish's book. **You have to laugh at yourself. We have to face our fears, trust our bodies, and be as prepared as we can be.** There is nothing you can do when "shit" happens, because it is going to happen. No one else is afraid of you eliminating, so you might as well accept it (especially now that you know I am just going to lie about it, anyway).

whatcha bringin'?

H ERE IS ANOTHER QUESTION I get asked a lot. "What should I pack?" We are obviously talking about packing for hospitals or birthing clinics. There is nothing to pack if you are having a home birth. Having said that, there is a list of birthing supplies you will need to have on hand before you go into labor at home; but that is a different matter.

Usually, your hospital bag is a typical overnight bag with any additional items one might want to bring for Baby. However, I have noticed that the more moms research, the more they end up bringing. Eventually, their bag is no longer intended for a one-night stay; it is a representation of their very being in luggage form. Some of the items I have seen women (and their families) bring have been quite amusing.

First off, we have to talk about what to wear. *Wait a sec, what to wear? Isn't that obvious? Nope.* Many women decide that they want to feel more comfortable and stylish while giving birth, and, let's face it, Heidi Klum, J. Lo, or Princess Di could not make those hospital gowns look good. However, I do recall a client who ordered her own "fashionable" hospital gown. It was black with big white polka dots, pink trim, and a matching bow for her hair. She looked like a pregnant Barbie doll. *FABULOUS!*

If you are going to wear a gown, you can bring your own bedtime gown complete with handy buttons for nursing like most of my clients do. If you are not wearing a comfy nightgown, then most likely you will be in a sports bra or nursing bra with leisure shorts or pants hanging below the belly. Be mindful though. With tops and bottoms instead of a gown, you might wind up giving birth in a bra soggy from the bath, and having the bottoms removed over and over again. I am sorry to say, ladies, you cannot have a vaginal exam with your panties still on. Maybe I will invent some soft but sturdy panties that can easily open and close from the front with Velcro... *Oh wait, that's a diaper. Moving on.*

I have seen lots of cardigans packed for easy removal because a laboring mom's body temp is wildly unpredictable. There is the oversized husband's t-shirt, a beach cover-up, a toga (not even kidding), and of course, "buck-nekkid." *Remember, I'm a Texan.*

One of my favorites though was a modest client named Lucy who wanted to be in the bathtub but not naked. She wore a hot pink birthing bikini. The top was a halter-top style, and the bottom was a wrap-around skirt with no built-in panties. It was genius, and she was one smoking hot mama! When I posted the pics from Lucy's birth, I had more people ask for that company's website than about the actual birth!

While laboring, most women want a pleasant atmosphere in which to give birth. Typically, the room is still and quiet, except maybe music playing; the TV is rarely on. I have had a few husbands turn on "the game," but it was muted. I also had a client that watched "The Walking Dead" while laboring. I'm still freaked out over that one. Felicia, though, had a very good reason for the TV to be on. I have had several friends, and probably four or five clients, that have appeared on the hit show, *Fixer Upper*. Felicia and her husband were some of those clients. It just so happened that Felicia's episode aired the same day she was being induced. So, naturally, we watched Chip and Jo do their magic while Felicia did hers. It was perfect!

For most clients, the only sound they want to hear during labor is music. This is not just any playlist. It is "their" playlist. The birthing playlist is a necessity for a lot of women, and they have poured hours into this inspirational musical conglomeration. Most of these playlists are pretty similar with lots of peaceful nature music, complete with distant raindrops in the background.

I remember one birth where my client, Suzannah, had chosen a "station" on Pandora, and what started as sweet raindrops turned into gusting winds, loud thunder clapping, and lightning striking every tree in the darn forest. I jumped, Suzannah's husband giggled, and she was just swaying away with this tropical storm in her hospital room. Pretty sure the staff got some complaints about that one.

You have to be careful, though, on what you choose to have playing during labor. You may never hear these songs the same way again. They could be ruined forever. I made the mistake of putting together a worship tape (yes, I am that old), and anytime I tried to listen to it again, I would get so anxious and agitated. If I hear "Breathe (I'm Desperate for You)" one more time, I am going to burn the tape and write a letter to Michael W. Smith.

"Dear Mr. Smith, Am I supposed to feel despairing and exhausted while listening to this song? I have a sudden urge to strangle someone. Is this a normal response?"

All jokes aside, I had a huge crush on MWS in my junior high years. I rode to the church potluck in an old yellow bus listening to him on my Walkman. I even married a Michael W... shout out to Michael Wade Burgess!

As a doula, I have heard some pretty diverse playlists. Let's see, we have had:

Betty with some elevator "hip-hop" Muzak; *Brilliant.*

Priscilla with show tunes such as "La Vie Boheme A," from the musical, *Rent*; and she knew all the words.

Ginger who played Zumba music, and we danced to PitBull and Shakira. There is actual video footage of this.

Liza who enjoyed her Disney animated soundtrack. *I am glad someone did.*

And my personal favorite...

Claire's "Wind Beneath My Wings" by Bette Midler on a repeat loop. *I should have asked for more money.*

What about the rest of your stuff? My advice has always been to pack how you would pack if you were going out of town for the weekend. Keep it simple and add anything you might want for Baby.

Here is my Top Five list of things I have seen to be helpful:

Carmex
Hair ties
Cardigan or sweater
Gum or mints
Energy snacks

Life-altering stuff, right? Sometimes my simple advice, however, gets translated into… two suitcases for mom, two duffle bags for dad, and two bags for Baby.

For example:

We have the work bag complete with laptop, chargers, ten files full of paper, and a giant notebook. One client's husband, Gary, even brought his folding table to set up all his gear. *Like there's not enough tables in a hospital room as it is.*

There is the essential oils tote bag loaded with all 167 oils offered in the promo special.

And of course, the snack bag filled with cupcakes from Nothing Bundt Cakes... *Yes, please...* or wasabi nuts and turmeric candy... *No, thanks.*

My brother did not like the snacks that my sister-in-law packed, so he brought in his own burrito. He was quickly dismissed by my sister-in-law after breathing in her face a refried-bean odor. *Come on, bro!*

But the best food story is when a family brought in and cooked their roast in the hospital's essential oil crockpot. Not sure if that is ridiculous or inspirational.

All the extra items that people lug into the hospital room can most certainly be useful and necessary. I mean, why not bring those comfort items? I have seen magnetic acupuncture ear balls that you squeeze during a contraction... *you sure about that?* I have also seen a rebozo - which is basically a tricked-up blanket used in different positions to manipulate Baby and provide relief to mom. One client, Esther, brought her own comforter from home. Again, create what feels normal to you!

Finally, I think my favorite item brought to a birth came from one of the dads, Stuart. He and his wife were repeat-clients, and after the baby was born, he waited for the nurse to leave, then pulled out something large from his bag. He had snuck in a bottle of whiskey for us to take shots (that's right, plural). All I will say about that is the styrofoam hospital cups are much larger than shot glasses!

To sum up, you can bring pretty much whatever you want because the goal is to feel normal, relaxed, and even pampered. So you do you, Elise, and bring your own massage therapist who doubles as Chris Hemsworth . . . or is it Chris Pine . . . no, maybe it's Chris Evans. No matter. It's a Chris, and I'm down.

CHAPTER 5

birth plans

---

*Y*OU MAY BE THINKING, what about all the planning and important decisions that need to be made before birth? **Way before making it to the birthing room, most expectant mamas start with planning their birth experience.** Some women make this their full-time job and take it very seriously. I mentioned earlier that you can choose to give birth at a hospital with a doctor or a midwife. You can also choose a birthing center or at home with a midwife. So, what is the difference?

Both OB/GYNs and midwives are trained to deliver babies. The biggest difference between them is that midwives do not perform surgery, namely C-sections. The focus in their schooling or training is also different. Doctors are well-versed and knowledgeable about interventions, procedures, and medications, while midwives are trained more specifically for natural approaches to childbirth. There is more to it than that, but that is the gist.

Besides choosing where you want to have your baby and whether or not you will use a doctor or a midwife, having a birth plan is at the top of most mom's priority lists. Put simply, a birth plan is basically a list of dos and don'ts. **As women research options, listen to others, and attend classes, they start to see the bigger picture when it comes to natural childbirth.** They read something and identify with the author's experience, then begin the process of discovering how they would want to move forward.

Here are some of the considerations you might find.

Interventions: what are they, and can I refuse them?

Induction: is it necessary, and are there other ways to start labor besides medication?

Drugs: do you want to address pain with medication?

Epidural: is it safe, and do I want to use it as an option for pain relief?

Monitoring: do I have to be attached to tubes and cords?

Moving: do I have to stay in the bed, or can I walk around?

Delivery: how do you push, and can I try different positions?

What about preeclampsia, VBAC, Hep-Lock, AROM, augmentation, vacuum, forceps, episiotomy, photography, attendees, delayed cord clamping, immediate skin to skin, Erythromycin, vitamin K shot, placenta encapsulation, circumcision? Believe it or not, the list goes on.

It is easy to see why a mom-to-be could get really tripped up, confused, and overwhelmed by all of these choices. While I could tell you all of my thoughts about each one of these things, I am not going to because that is just not entertaining. I will, however, address a few.

Induction is a way to start labor. This could be Pitocin through your IV, AROM, which is breaking your water, or midwives might use Black Cohosh, a medicinal herb, coupled with walking. **Y'all know what my answer is to get things going - SEX!**

How about pain relief? As you get further into the book, you will see that I always try to distract my clients and get them focused on other ways to bring relief. **I am not saying to not use medication or an epidural, I just think they should be used as a last resort.**

Monitoring and moving go hand-in-hand. You can always ask for a hep-lock or saline lock, instead of an IV, and most hospitals have portable monitors. This will allow you to move freely. **Unless there is a medical reason, you do NOT have to be stuck in the bed.**

With delivery and pushing, you have to have a totally different mindset from the focused relaxation you had during labor. You cannot just sit back and rest anymore. There is work to do. Let me go a little deeper.

There can be many voices guiding the mom during this time of pushing. I have learned over the years what some of the most effective directions can be for a mama to focus and find the "Sweet Spot." Yeah, I said it - SWEET SPOT. The Sweet Spot is that place where the pressure in your perineum and rectum must simultaneously push and relax in order to open up and allow the contraction to bring your baby down further into the birthing canal. This also brings the urge to push. It feels as crazy as it sounds. The more pressure, the more intensity, the more intensity, the more you want to get away from it all. The key, of course, is to go towards the pressure and not away from it.

You should see some of the looks and hear some of the responses I get when I say, "Okay mama, that pressure you feel, go towards that."

Here's the short list:

"Are you crazy, lady?!"

"That's gonna hurt like a mother!"

"You think I'm a fool? I don't want that feeling to last!"

"I'm ripping open as we speak!"

"How the hell am I supposed to do that?!"

"I'm dying and you expect me to what? Go into the light?"

They all basically mean the same thing: "Ummm, NO! Just NO"

Don't be haters. I've had to do it too. I get it. That bowling ball is not getting smaller. And I know, I know, you are still getting over the fact that you are going to poop!

How about when you hear the phrase, "Don't push"? WHAT THE WHAT?! That's right, you are being told to stop pushing at the very moment your body is pushing on its own.

Here is what happens when you tell a laboring mom, "Don't push":

"You did not just tell me to stop pushing and wait on the doctor! I finally found the Sweet Spot."

"Oh, okay. How 'bout you stop having blonde hair and stop talking?"

"Do you know what I'm doing here? I am trying to have a baby. I don't need a doctor. I need a baby, 'cause I need to be done!"

"He's comin' out of my AAAAAA…!"

"OOOOOOOOKKAAAAAAAAYYYYY!

HHHHMMMMMMMMMAAAAAAAAA! I'LL
STOOOOOOOOOOOOOOOOOOOOOOOOOOP
PUUUUUUUUUSHHHAAAAAAAAAANG!"
"Oh, you can just stick it."

There are really only a few good reasons to
stop pushing. One is to allow Baby's head to stretch
the perineum, so you do not tear. Another might be
for a medical or safety reason like removing the
cord from around Baby's neck. Beyond that, telling
you not to push is usually to allow the medical staff
time to get into the room and get ready.

Here's the thing, I figured out pretty quickly
that every Labor and Delivery nurse knows how to
catch a baby. I may or may not be letting my clients
in on that little secret. I plead the Fifth! **It is not the
laboring mom's responsibility to make sure
everyone is in place before she pushes her baby
out.**

Go ahead, mama, speak your truth.

There are things that I believe women should
be informed on and have a sense of what they think
they might want or need when it comes to birth

plans. Every woman has the right to certain desires or strong opinions about any one of these procedures or issues. However, I do advise my clients not to have a soapbox or a deep passion for EVERY item on this list. **You do not have to feel strongly about something just because someone else does.** Being adamant that your hospital band is placed on your left hand and not your right might be a poor use of your energy. And yes, I did have a client who most definitely cared about her band, and she DID receive it on the hand she wanted. As it should be.

When you look at your birth plan as a whole, you should be able to see what kind of birth you want. There should be a theme, or it should match your personality, so to speak. Most people have heard of the different personality tests. Here's an example of a Type A, Enneagram 1, Myers-Briggs ISTJ client in action.

I received a call from this potential client who was looking into hiring a doula because she knew exactly what she wanted and wanted to make sure she was going to get it. Y'all, I do not have that much power. Rhonda hired me before she was even pregnant. I received a four-page birth plan by email six months before her due date. She had done her homework and taken three different childbirth classes to be ready. The first page was a chart with every intervention or decision a woman could make. It was color-coded and corresponded with page two which went into detail of what her understanding was of each item listed. On page three, she rated the importance of every decision that would be made, and on page four was an essay summarizing the whole birth. Needless to say, I knew exactly what I was getting with this client and could not wait to work with her. I just want to say, I LOVED working with Rhonda! She was funny, intelligent, engaged, and kicked labor's butt! You go, ISTJ/Type-A/E1!

Some of my sensitive thinkers have written manuscripts explaining not only what they want but why they want it. Birth plans from these clients are usually very thorough and contain very detailed experiences.

Shelby hired me for her second birth and relayed some things that she learned after her first birth experience. After some childbirth classes, she realized she wanted something different for this birth. Shelby had a beautiful heart, mind, and spirit, and put together her version of a birth plan. Here are some of her thoughts.

"After some research, discussion, and soul searching, I have put together my ideal birth. It's based on facts, experience, and my desires. Below I've written out my wishes and expectations concerning the doula's role: Here are several ways to promote positivity and care along with some phrases you can use; comfort measures - here are five or six options that I'm sure will help; ways I want to labor and ways I want to deliver; I've also included the reasons why I don't want to use certain strategies to promote better results; finally my disappointments with the hospital staff - please note that I will be aggressive in my communicating this go-round."

Keep in mind, I just told you the topics; I did not include all seventeen paragraphs with the details. I really hope that Shelby writes a book one day because she is an excellent communicator, and her detailed descriptions leave no doubt to the reader what she is trying to convey.

Another client, Sandra, brought six copies of her birth plan - one for her nurse, the charge nurse, the doctor, her husband, another one for me, and an extra, just in case. She then proceeded to read it out loud to all of us.

When she was finished, she said, "Are there any questions? Do I need to go over anything again?"

I think you covered it. Now let's make it happen.

The creative, "go with the flow" women have pictures attached to each point written out. There might be a total of five to seven things they actually care about. They are not so much married to the plan as they are of each person's understanding and connection to their process. They do not want to "rock the boat," and their fear is that their wishes may not be relative when the time comes.

Here is Mary's birth plan:

(attached picture)

Induction - I would really like to avoid being induced. I've heard that Pitocin makes labor ten times harder. If I'm thirty-six-weeks pregnant and still haven't delivered, then I would like to revisit the conversation. *Wait, you think you should have had your baby by thirty-six weeks? We need to have another conversation.*

(picture)

Pain relief - my goal is to avoid pain meds and an epidural. Of course, if I just can't do it anymore, then I'm not opposed to trying them. While I would prefer the nurses not to offer me any drugs, I don't consider myself Superwoman and am open to suggestions.

FYI - trying to "avoid" pain medication but being "open to suggestions" is like trying to avoid a cup of coffee in Starbucks while smelling each one of the flavors that are being served that day. Also, there is not any "trying" when it comes to pain medication. There is just denying or partaking. *Enjoy your meds, mama.*

(pictures)

Positions - I'd like for my body to decide what position to labor and deliver in. Having said that, I'm not a demanding person so if you think something else would work better then let me know.

I want to point out that it was not just a picture, but several pictures of twelve different positions. In one picture, the loved one (or doula, I guess) was sitting on a chair. The laboring woman was sitting on his or her lap, facing towards this person, not away. Her rear-end was hanging low between the loved one/doula's legs. *Hey y'all, don't be weird.*

(picture)

Episiotomy - I do not want to be cut. I'm truly scared of this procedure! If Baby appears to be stuck, then I'm sure it will be okay if you have to use this option. *I'm starting to think that everything is actually on the table for Mary.*

(picture)

Skin to skin - I definitely want for my baby to be placed on my chest as soon as he is born. I'm so looking forward to this bonding time! I'm asking that only an emergency would prohibit me from having this time. *That's what I'm talkin' about, Mama.*

Lastly, there are the indecisive mamas like Enneagram Type 9s or an INFP on the Myers Briggs. These sweethearts have a hard time making a decision and do not want to be locked in. It all depends on how they are going to feel in the moment. Their birth plan is probably a half-page, handwritten, outline with eraser marks, scratch outs, and arrows drawn from one point to another.

Honestly, some should not even bother with a birth plan. Y'all, I had a client bring in her birth plan, and it said, "DON'T DIE!"

A birth plan can be very helpful. **Remember, it is a guide to assist you in discovering what you want out of childbirth.** No one really knows, though, how it will all play out. What we do know is that childbirth is an adventure and extremely rewarding.

CHAPTER 6

what's that you say?

*O*H, THE THINGS I have seen and the things I have heard! The above title is meant to be read like a cheerleader chanting that old favorite, "What's that you say? I said, 'Let me see you clap your hands!' What's that you say? I said, 'OO, ah ah, AH-OO, ah ah, AH-OO, ah ah AH-OO,' ONE MORE TIME!" That is what goes through my mind sometimes when, during a client's labor, I hear a FABULOUS one-liner!

When my client, Gretchen, saw the forceps pulled out of their package she hollered, "GEEZE! Those look like King Kong's salad tongs! Y'all are gonna have to figure out somethin' else 'cause, I can tell you right now, those are NOT gonna fit up my veegee-hole!"

Grown women with nicknames for their female anatomy crack me up: "Va-jay-jay," "Boo-boo doll," "Va-va-voom," "Gina," "Gi-Gi," "Tookie," "Coochie," "My V," "My Special," "Down There," "Lady Bits," and "Vera Wang" just to name a few.

What's that you say? *I said, "Let me hear you say VAGINA." What's that you say?*

One of my clients was a friend of mine and someone I had mentored for a time. My husband and I had also done marriage counseling for her and her husband. Labor was hard, but she was following a great pattern of breathing. It was time to push, and I was coaching her on breathing in deeply through her nose, then holding the air in and bearing down.

"Okay, Sarah. Now you're gonna fill your lungs with a good deep breath in through your nose, and, instead of blowing it all out, trap that power. Don't let the air out, and then push down in your bottom."

She drew a deep breath, then blew the air out

through her vibrating lips like a horse. Her face turned deep red as she glanced at me, embarrassed by the noise that just came out of her mouth.

"Oh no! I'm sorry I didn't obey you, Micah."

Obey me? I'm not sure you understand the concept of coaching. I'm not yo' mama, I'm yo' doula, and I'm here for YOU. Whatever works, works! You can quote me on that one.

"Girl! I'm just giving some direction. We will find what works for you. You got this!"

She proceeded to make this motorboat sound with every contraction and every push.

It was effective because that baby was born in about ten minutes! After the baby was in my client's arms, she let out a sigh of relief. For a second there, I thought I heard a whinny.

What's that you say? *I said, "Let me hear your* MOTORBOAT!" *What's that you say?*

During labor, I intentionally hold back on some of the better options of relief; I dangle them like a carrot. I give a twenty- to thirty-minute game plan, then tell my client when we are done, there will be a reward. For example, you can get into the shower after we walk the halls. It is like in prison when you get a pack of cigarettes for doing someone's toilet chore. Except, I am nicer than a prison guard, and no crime was committed on this joyous occasion.

Tammy had just completed three contractions on the potty. (If you do not know already, you are going to want to know this: **The toilet is one of the best, but also hardest, places to have a contraction.** It opens up your pelvis in a way that nothing else can). Baby had dropped quite a bit, and mama could feel every second of it.

"You're doing so good, Tammy. You're almost done, and then you're gonna get that popsicle."

Believe it or not, a popsicle is a hot commodity on the Labor and Delivery floor. That's right, an orange popsicle awaits you once you have disarmed the guard. I mean, endured three contractions on the potty.

"Okay girl, here's your popsicle. Enjoy!"

"MMMMMMMM! This is better than sex!"

I'm sure it is...

What's that you say? *I said, "She prefers a POP-SI-CLE." What's that you say?*

Cheri was a repeat client, and I was attending the birth of her second. Her labor was going fast, and she announced she had to poop. *Oh, good! Mama like.* She went into the bathroom and shut the door. After a few minutes, I could hear some "pushy" sounds.

"Cheri, you okay? Are you pushing?"

"I'm good. Hhhmmmmmmmmmmm."

"Cheri? It sounds like you're bearing down."

"I'm feeling a little pressure, but I'm okay."

I started becoming doubtful. After a couple of minutes, I could clearly hear Cheri pushing.

"Hey, Cheri, I'm comin' in."

Cheri was on the bathroom floor on her hands and knees grunting and pushing. This baby was coming! I called for her husband, Gerald, to come give me a hand.

"Cheri, let us help you get to the bed."

"No. I want to stay here!"

"UUUUUUMMMMMMM. Let's not have a baby on the bathroom floor."

Gerald and I each took an arm to help her up. Would you believe she dropped and flopped like a three-year-old having a tantrum? We had to hold her and pull her to the bed as she became deadweight. You would think her response would have been something like, "I'm so tired," "Thank you for helping me," or even "The baby is coming." NOPE.

"Why can't y'all just leave me alone? I hate you guys."

You'll be glad once Baby is here that we literally dragged your a** to the bed. You're welcome.

What's that you say? *I said, "OO, ah ah, You're RUDE! girlfriend, You're RUDE! it's okay, ME TOO!" ONE MORE TIME! What's that you say?*

One particular coping method that sticks out to me came from my client, Carol. I was assisting her with some breathing techniques, and she developed a rhythm all on her own. She was focused and going through labor like it was nothing. Most women during a contraction stop moving and take deep breaths to fully relax their shoulders, face, and legs. Through every contraction, Carol would thrust her arms straight down and flex her wrists with fingers spread upwards. She would scrunch her shoulders up to her cheeks and walk around the room on her tiptoes with a tense look on her face. She and her husband were chanting this rhythmic phrase together through almost every contraction until Baby was born:

"Sh-sh-it. Sh-sh-it. Sh-sh-iiiiiiit! SH-SH-IIIIIIIT!"

I will admit, it was a pretty catchy beat. *Gotta do whatcha gotta do!*

What's that you say? *"SHIT, sh-sh, SH-IT, sh-sh, SH-IT, sh-sh, SH-IT!" ONE MORE TIME! What's that you say?*

The dads say some funny one-liners as well. While I was being born, my dad was in the room with my mom, which was not a very common choice at the time. My mom wanted to give birth naturally, so whether he wanted to or not, he was going to be there. My mom was pushing, and it got to the part when you can see about a silver dollar size of the baby's head.

My dad loudly exclaimed, "Oh no! Is that a tumor? Somebody do something! Look, it's a tumor!" *Take some childbirth classes, dad. Geeze!*

What's that you say? *I said, "Seems like you're UN-ED-U-CAT-ED." What's that you say?*

I remember going to an interview with Allanah and her husband, Seth, to see if they wanted to hire me as their doula. They were a little late to the party because she was already thirty-four weeks pregnant. We had lunch, and they hired me on the spot.

Around 4 p.m., Seth called me. "Well, you must be really good at what you "adoula" 'cause Allanah's water just broke."

That's right, I AM that good.

What's that you say? *I said, "Let me hear you say 'DOU-LA'!" What's that you say?*

My client, Velva, and her husband, Troy, were pretty young and having their first baby. Her labor was very long and very difficult. We were going on hour sixteen, and she was finally talking about feeling pressure. Troy had been an excellent support to Velva. I knew he was tired, and I think he was also getting more anxious.

When Velva started to bear down a little, Troy announced, "Ladies, I'm gonna need a minute."

He then turned around and walked into their bathroom. *Okay... yeah, Troy, you take a minute. Your wife is about to give birth but go ahead and catch your breath.*

We then heard Troy from the bathroom lamenting. "DEAR GOD! I'M IN TROUBLE!"

It was just now dawning on Troy what he had gotten himself into. *Little too late, bro.*

What's that you say? *I said, "Let me see you say AMEN!" What's that you say?*

One of my repeat clients was having her second baby, and it was happening fast. She was complaining a little about her back being sore. I started to massage her back and apply a little counter-pressure.

About four contractions later she said, "That feels so good! I would pay money for this."

Her husband replied, "You did."

Don't worry, gratuity is included.

What's that you say? *I said, "GRATUITY INCLUDED." What's that you say?*

And finally, the best one-liner I have ever heard was from a veteran dad. This was my client Chrissy's third birth, and her labor was progressing beautifully. Her husband, Lionel, was a fantastic coach and right there with her every step of the way.

Chrissy began moaning, and I knew she was getting close to delivery. I suggested she try going to the restroom and have a few contractions on the potty. By now, you should know what I am doing.

"OOOOOH! OOOOOOOH! OOOOOOOOH! OOOOOOOOOOOOOOOOH!"

"That's it, Chrissy. Perfect! Just breathe through these."

It was clear by her tone, her face, and body language that she was in transition. Lionel and I began helping her back to the bed when she stopped at the edge and started to bear down. The nurse asked her if she felt pressure and was pushing. *Are you and I looking at the same patient? Let's GO!*

"Chrissy, I need you to stop pushing and wait for the doctor."

"Well, that's not gonna happen!"

We successfully got her into the bed, and she began pushing fully.

"Lionel! Take my panties off!"

"Now where have I heard that before?" Lionel grinned.

He did NOT just say that out loud! Lionel's got game. I'm dyin'.

"AHHHHHHHHHH! HEEEEEEEEEEEE'S COOOMING!"

The nurse frantically began preparing, "OH MY! Let me get my gloves on!"

It was too late for that! Lionel reached down, caught his baby, and put him on mama's chest.

"BABE! I'm so proud of you! He's here!"

"Did you just make a SEXUAL innuendo while I was giving birth to your son?"

Don't answer that Lionel. She's gonna forget it all soon enough.

What's that you say? *I said… never mind, I don't want to hear it. Save it for the bedroom.*

How many situations are we ever in where there are no filters in what we say? That is what at times makes so much of the birthing process humorous and entertaining.

CHAPTER 7

sweet southern mouths

*O*KAY, BY NOW Y'ALL know that I am a Texan, and many of my clients are Southern. If you are not sure what that means, then let me try and give you an idea. First of all, a true Southern woman has a bit of an accent where the letter "e" sounds more like the short vowel sound "i" (as in "git" instead of "get"), and the "g" gets dropped from "-ing" to make "thinkin'" instead of "thinking." Oh yeah, and one-syllable words are more like three-syllable words. See if you can read the sentence below:

"I've bin awl oover Tex's y'awll lookin' fer thu bayest swate tay fer may ainnd mye baybee."

Translation:

"I have been all over Texas, you guys, looking for the best sweet tea for me and my baby (man)."

We say "fixin' to," "ain't," "reckon," and "howdy," which translated means: "about to," "not," "I think," and "hello." My daddy used to say things like, "Just a stone's throw away," "Lord willin', and the creek don't rise," "Quicker than you can shake a stick at," and "This ain't my first rodeo."

We tend to be very respectful, friendly, and polite. We wave at every car (truck, rather) that we pass by, including strangers, and will probably strike up a conversation with you in line just about anywhere. One time, a friend who was from up north and I were texting about an upcoming event she had planned. At one point, she asked me if I could bring chips and dip (most of the time this means tortilla chips and salsa). My reply was simply, "Yes, ma'am." Her response was immediate, "You are making me feel old and frumpy." Oops. I swear I was not trying to offend her. I apologized, of course, being the good Southern woman that I am. I then wondered how many others I had unintentionally offended. This is a Southern woman's worst nightmare!

However, you should definitely be offended if

you hear any of these phrases: "jist fell off the turnip truck," "all hat 'n no cattle," "one brick shy of a load," "she is libel ta hit ya plum into next week," "raised in a barn," "can't ride and chew at the same time," or "worth about as much as teats on a bull." But the absolute worst thing a Southerner can say to you is "well, bless your heart." It is basically ridicule or insincere sentiment for your stupidity concerning your pitiful predicament. Sorry fellow Texans, you may be receiving some hate mail *(I mean, hate TEXTS; showin' my age here again).*

So, back to my Southern Belles who come into the birthing room smiling and greeting everyone with a "Hey, how y'all doin'?" They are also probably saying "Thank you" and "Yes, ma'am" at every turn. *Gotta love it!* I will say, over the years, I have been highly entertained by some of these Southern mouths.

One of my clients, Josie, was a classic beauty, had all her ducks in a row, and when she spoke, it sounded like pure honey. She had a big, beautiful home and could be the poster child for Southern hospitality. When Josie arrived at the hospital, she was getting to know the staff and, in particular, her nurse, Lorraine. Now, Lorraine was old school, very methodical, and everything she did was by the book. She wanted to check Josie every hour to make sure she was progressing. Vaginal exams are the pits, y'all, and Lorraine was not very gentle or good at these.

"Okay now, Josie, hold still and let me try and find your cervix."

"OOOH, ouch! Careful."

"I know, I'm sorry. I just can't seem to reach it. Let me go up a little higher."

Under Josie's breath, she mouthed, "Ouch, damn it!"

It is not all that uncommon for a woman to cuss during childbirth. I just find it especially humorous when she is a Sweet Southern Belle. Lorraine quickly removed her arm out of my client's vagina and gave no report as to her progress.

Now Lorraine was one of those nurses that still believed laboring mamas were supposed to stay in the bed.

"Okay now, Josie, let's get your temperature and vitals. Everything looks pretty good. We'll need to go ahead and leave the blood pressure cuff on."

"Miss Lorraine, I was hopin' to walk around a bit now that you've gotten several good reads on the baby's and my vitals."

"Well, Josie, it's much easier to follow Baby's heart rate when you are sitting still. We want to make sure Baby stays happy."

"Umm, yes ma'am, but let's make sure that I stay happy if you don't mind. Thank you sooo much."

Now y'all, when a Southern woman states what she wants, then follows it up with "Thank you SOOO much," she is not expressing her appreciation for you or thanking you for a job well done. If there is a painted smile on her face, and her head is tilted to the side just a little, then she basically just told you, "I don't care who you are, but I'm about to get what I want, so you can stick it where the sun don't shine."

"Well, let me go check with your doctor and see what she says."

As Lorraine walked out the door Josie mouthed to me, "What the f*ck?!"

At this point, I was trying not to bust a gut laughing! When the door shut, I spewed out an awkward laugh, then heard this polished woman roll the "F"-word and a buffet of cuss words off her tongue like they were her native language. Seriously, it was a Chris Rock comedy special in that hospital room.

Lorraine returned and gave permission for Josie to get out of bed for a little while. Thank goodness. However, it was short-lived. After about twenty minutes, Lorraine returned.

"Well, I'm not getting a very good read on baby while you're moving around. Time to get back in bed so we can find his heart rate."

I chimed in quickly with an assist. "Hey Josie, weren't you just tellin' me that you needed to empty your bladder?"

"Oh yes. Yes, I was."

"Lorraine, I'll come get you as soon as she's finished."

Lorraine agreed and walked out of the room. For the next hour, Josie allegedly had the longest bowel movement of her life. *When you gotta go, you gotta go.*

Finally, Lorraine came back into the room and insisted that she get her vitals and check on Baby. While Josie was making her way back to the bed, Lorraine informed her that she would be checking her progress again.

Josie replied, without hesitation, "That would be a HAYYYLLL NO!"

That's Southern for "HELL NO!"

Josie made it through labor, and her Sweet Southern Belle was born. The nurse laid the baby on her chest, and all the adoring smiles appeared as this baby had her hand resting on mom's breast. *So sweet...* No wait, she was flipping us off! There was no doubting who her mama is.

The next Southern beauty is Grace and her husband, Howard. They were graduate students and very young. Some of the sweetest, calmest, most proper people I have ever met. It is for people like her that the phrase "syrupy sweet" was made. Even the volume of her voice was unusually quiet. At our interview, I kept having to lean in and strain just so that I could hear her. She was almost whispering. Her responses to me were short and simple, laced with smiles and sighs. It was so very tender, and I was looking forward to working with her.

Fast forward to the birth. I arrived to find Grace breathing just like I had taught her in our client class. Slow deep breaths, inhale through your nose and blow out long and slow. I watched her for a bit, and finally decided that we needed to change something. She was not really comfortable, and there was not a natural rhythm yet. For early labor, it seemed her breathing was extremely difficult, and she was already getting tired.

"Grace, let's tweak your breathing. I'm not convinced this is working. How about breathing normally, without exaggerating the inhale and exhale process?"

She responded calmly with her soft voice and a pleasant smile. "I will certainly try that. Thank you."

Next thing I knew, her eyes and mouth were closed, and her chest was barely moving. She was having a contraction and I could not hear anything. Wow!

"That's much better, Micah, thank you."

She did this for the ENTIRE birth! I should have expected nothing less from Grace. Such poise. Here is what made this sweet Southern mouth so funny: consistently throughout birth, coming from this petite darling sweetheart, were the loudest belches you have ever heard.

"BRR-AAAOOOUU-RRRP!"

I literally jumped!

"Excuse me, please." She said it as if she tapped someone on the shoulder so that she could pass by.

"BWWWWOOOOUUUUURRRRP! Excuse me."

I smirked and looked over at her husband, Howard, to see if he noticed at all. He was unfazed by her outburst. Hours had passed by and through every contraction there was absolutely no effort whatsoever from Grace. Then all of a sudden, like a drunken cowboy rockin' on his back porch... BAAAAAUUUUURRRRP!

My next client was a doctor, Dr. Eliza Do'Little. She was a tremendous blessing in our community because of her involvement with various clubs and charities. She was heavily invested in her church and was very patriotic; true attributes to a good Southern woman. This well-respected woman was having her second baby, and today was Game Day. When she called me, I could hear that she was already in labor. She was just arriving and talking to the front desk clerk swaying back and forth when I met her at the hospital.

"I'm in active labor, and I need to get back to the L&D floor right away."

"It's gonna be just a minute, ma'am. I need to get you registered."

She was calm and confident when she replied. "I have already pre-registered."

"Okay, tell me your social security number and your address?"

"Wait, what? What does that matter?" She started another contraction, so her husband responded to the question.

The hospital staff member continued. "Got it. Now I need to see your ID and your insurance card."

By then my client was clearly frustrated. Panting through her contraction, she managed to say, "I have already pre-registered. You have all this information already."

She began breathing hard and pacing, trying to keep her composure.

"Yes ma'am, I understand but we still need to verify a couple of things in order to let you back there."

You know how they say teachers do not always make the best students? In the same way, doctors do not always make the best patients.

The admittance questions persisted. "Who is your doctor?"

My client continued breathing through a contraction and ignored the question.

"Excuse me, ma'am, your doctor?"

My client held up her finger, (no, not that finger) gave her the death glare, took a deep breath, and said., "Excuse you! I'm in the middle of a contraction! Open the blankety-blank-blank-blank doors! I'm clearly in labor!"

She actually said, "blankety-blank-blank-blank."

"As soon as I get all of your info down, then I can let you back."

"This is ridiculous! Do you know who I am? I am Dr. Eliza Do'Little, and you have all of my information. I pre-registered, and you need to open those doors right now!"

Her husband spoke up. "Her doctor is Dr. Trivago, and can I finish answering the questions so that she can head on back?"

We had now progressed to yelling. "No! What's the point in pre-registering if you're gonna have to stand out here and answer all these questions!? Uh, meanwhile, I think my water just broke! I repeat, I am Dr. Do'Little and I'm gonna be makin' some phone calls…"

"Oh, uh, yes, ma'am. Go ahead. Let them know you think your water broke. Is there anything else I can do for you?"

"You can go to… well, somewhere else besides your desk!"

We can't always have it together, look the part, be graceful, or be the hostess with the mostest. We try to be friendly and understanding at all times. But sometimes, you just "Don't Mess with Texas," or with the Southern Belles that live there!

CHAPTER 8

sobbing mommies

---

*E*VERY WOMAN DEALS WITH her birth in her own way. For some, it just seems so easy; we will get back to them. But for most of us, we can agree that birth is hard. The truth is, most of us get vocal at some point during childbirth, like grunting or even yelling. I have had a few though that have cried; actually sobbed for several minutes. I am not just talking about tearing up, got a hug, and then moved on... I mean boo-hooing. A couple of mamas stand out to me in this unique way.

We will start with Evelyn. This young mama hired me because she knew her husband, Brodie, was not going to be a very big support system for her. More of his story is in a later chapter. Anyway, jump ahead to the day of the birth, and she had been laboring for a while and doing great. We were all the way into active labor and expecting transition soon. This sweet little mama was very tired, and something happened (I am still not sure exactly what it was) to set her off. After one of her contractions, she started to weep. Yep, you heard me, WEEP!

"EEeeeeeh-aaaaaaah-huh-huh! Uhuh, huh, huh! Aaaaaaaah-huh-huh-huh!"

All I could do was just stare at her. I was trying to assess her quickly, but all I could think is that it sounded like a fake cry. I continued to watch her as I chose my words carefully. This was definitely my first experience of a woman weeping. Sure, I have had clients shed a few tears, but as quickly as they would come, they would leave. It was more of a stress release. This was different.

"Buuuuuuuuh-haaa-haaaaaaaaaaaa!"

Hmmmmmmmm...

Another contraction hit.

She took a deep breath in through her nose just like all the other times before and, "Huuuuuuuh-huuuuuuh-huuuuuuh... Aaaaaaaaaaaaa-huh-huh..." She grabbed another deep breath through her streaming tears and headed right back to the next contraction. "Huuuuuuuh-aaaaaaaaaaah-huh-huh… Buuuuuaaaaaaah-huuuuuh-huh!"

Y'all see how I just keep adding repetitive vowels to create these sobbing sounds? Work with me here.

This girl continued to bawl in the middle of her contractions! Over and over again, during the contractions, between the contractions; it was non-stop. I was not exactly sure what to say. I knew I needed to comfort her but I felt like I was looking at my four-year-old daughter who did not want to go to bed. **Nurturing is one thing, patronizing is a BIG no-no.** My strengths are empowering women and affirming them to do the job that is in front of them to do. So, I rejected the notion to stroke her head and say, "Aaaaawww, there, there."

"Evelyn? Can you hear me?" *(Come on out.)*

She did not answer. I started second-guessing my question. It was not like she was being hypnotized and reliving her first trip to the circus where she encountered a big scary clown; or hallucinating that she was heading down the rabbit hole with Alice and The Cheshire Cat. *Do not even try to tell me you liked Alice in Wonderland, and that you are not scared of clowns or that weird cat. I am just going to say it... DE-MON-IC!*

"Evelyn?"

Are you in there, Evelyn?

"Mmmmmmmmhhhhhh-huh-huh-aaaaaaah! Mmmmhhhhhh-huh-huuuuh-aaaaah!"

Guess not. Another contraction began.

"Aaaaaaarrrrrrrhhhhhhh-aaaaah-huh-hu-huh. III dooon't waaaant to dooo thissss aaaannyyyy-moooooore. Baaaaaaaaah-haaaaaa-haaaaaaa-huh!"

There she is. Now, this I can work with.

Typically, when a mama says, "I'm done, I can't do this," or "give me drugs," I don't panic. In fact, I long to hear these words. **More than likely, these words mean she IS about to be done. It is a great sign that helps me put a game plan together for the next few contractions before delivery.**

"Don't worry, Evelyn. I think you're almost done. I promise everything is good and right. Your baby is comin', and you're doing a great job."

Perfect timing. The doctor showed up, checked her cervix, and we were in business. It was time to have a baby. *No more tears now mama, gotta get to work.*

How about Ella? She was also a first-time mom who was definitely nervous about the whole natural childbirth process. I asked her several times while she was pregnant why she wanted to go natural. She always had the same answer. Her husband, Lenny, was concerned about the potential negative effects of drugs on the baby. I was a little concerned about Ella. Your husband wanting you to go the natural route is not going to be enough for you to withstand the physical and mental struggle that comes with childbirth. While I understand that this is his baby too, I am a pretty firm believer that if you are not the one doing the work or enduring the pain, then you should probably defer to what the mother believes she is capable of. That is my nice way of saying, "You better rethink this before you speak again, and then you might as well zip it!"

Ella's first call to me was to meet her at the hospital straight away.

Oh boy, that didn't take long.

I entered her room, and to my surprise, she was standing, smiling, and talking.

Hmmmmm, is she even in labor?

"Well, I'm 7 cm."

"That's great, Ella! You seem to be doing really well."

"I guess so."

A contraction came, and I watched her breeze through it. I was truly impressed. I misjudged her bigtime!

"That was excellent, Ella. You keep doing that and you're gonna make it."

She grinned with a sigh and proceeded to tell me that she was really scared about pushing. She was interrupted by another contraction. Once again, Ella did not show any signs of pain or doubt. This is great! She was going to be able to have the natural childbirth she was aiming for.

Wait a second. Another contraction began, this time, right on top of the other one. Ella was in transition.

"I'm not sure how much longer I can do this."

BINGO! Words I love to hear!

"Got it. Those are very close contractions. You may not have to be doing this much longer."

Another big contraction hit, and she actually moaned a little. *Beautiful! Textbook!* I did notice one thing, though. Ella was still standing, and she had her legs squeezed together at her upper thighs.

Well, that's not gonna work.

"Ella, you are absolutely killing it! I'm so proud of you! You've got this. I just want to adjust one thing that you're doing. You're squeezing your legs together, and you probably need to open them up a bit more. This will help you relax and give Baby more room to come down."

Frozen. She did not move, nod, or change anything. Yep, you guessed it, another contraction began. Again, she stood very quiet moaning and squeezing those legs together as tight as she could. Y'all recognize the problem here, right? Babies do not come out of your stomach like we believed when we were children. Not to mention, she was being counterproductive with the contractions and her amazingly fast labor.

"Ooooooooooh. I need to push."

"Perfect. Let's get the nurse and see where you're at."

We called for the nurse, and she came in to give Ella an exam. This was not easy. She would not open her legs AT ALL. The nurse explained that she was going to need her to relax and open her legs so that she could check. Y'all, large crocodile tears began streaming down her face.

"Ella? What's wrong? Everything is going great. It's just time to see what your body is doing."

Ella was crying and sniffling as the nurse and I tried to pry her legs open just enough for the nurse to get a few fingers in there.

"Okay, Ella. You're a nine."

"That's fantastic, girl! You can do this!"

There were more tears, and the crying turned into bawling.

"Ella, talk to me. What's going on?"

"It hurts, and I don't want to push. MMmmmhhhhhuuuuuh. I want an epidural!" That was a pushing sound, y'all.

Lenny spoke up. "No-no, Ella. Just listen to your 'adoula'."

First of all, I know that doula is a strange

word. I get called many variations of the word but, it's "doula," not "adoula." Second of all, this is not about YOU, Lenny. SHHHHHH.

Ella continued crying. "Booooooo-hoo-hoo!"

This wail was followed by a whimper and a snort.

"Hang on, Ella. Not quite time to push. Let's let those contractions finish doing their job."

Ella sat up on the bed, then stood to her feet, legs crossed, now sobbing.

"Uuuuuu-aaaaaaa-aaaaa-oooooooh!"

This went on for about thirty minutes. This poor, grown woman was totally overwhelmed and, honestly, I cannot blame her. I realized that she was "stuck" at nine centimeters because she had a little lip left on her cervix. This means she felt like pushing, but it was not time to push. I could not watch this suffering anymore. **I am NOT into torture, yo!** I knew of one thing we could do that would probably work, but those legs were like Fort Knox. *We're not gettin' in.*

I grabbed the charge nurse because Ella's nurse did not know how to move the lip out of the way while mama was pushing. I let her off the hook that time because she was a young nurse, but, people, let's get it together. You should know every trick in the book to assist your fellow sister in her hour of need! I began explaining to Ella what we were about to do.

Her first reaction was a whine followed by hyper-breaths.

"AAAaaaaaaa-hhaaaaaa-haaaaa." Sniveling and shaking.

"I know this seems scary, but I do not want you to have to do any more contractions like this. Are you ready to move on to the pushing stage?"

Cue contraction.

"MMmmmmmmmmhhhhuuuhhh. Booo-hooooo-hooooo. AAaaaaaaaauuuuuuugh." Now she was hyperventilating. "Okay."

Then the hard part: getting those legs unlocked.

Let me just say, through many tears, boo-hooing and snotty breathing, we were able to move that cervix out of the way, and Ella pushed her baby out in about ten minutes. The miracle of birth is about how our bodies are created to bring a human into the world. However, in this birth, the miracle was also the moment when that baby came out of mama, the zombie apocalypse ended, and life as we knew it returned.

Check that, life will never be the same.

Let's take a different angle on this topic and talk about Shelby. I was hired for her second birth because her first was extremely long and difficult. She opted for the epidural with her first and was looking for a totally different experience. Be careful what you wish for.

Now listen, most women will say that they want fast labor. Okay. Are you prepared for it to be fast and furious? I'm not kidding. It can be downright violent. Why?

Well, if you are having fast labor, then that means your body is changing and progressing quickly. It is working twice as fast, and this means the experience is twice as intense. You cannot really have one without the other.

Shelby called me the day of her delivery to tell me that her contractions were super intense, and she was headed to the hospital.

When I arrived, she was pacing, breathing deeply, and when she had a contraction, already wincing.

"Micah, I don't think I can do this. It's been so intense, and the contractions are so close together. I'm getting no breaks."

Look out! Another contraction began.

Shelby closed her eyes, took a deep breath, and tried to focus. She was struggling and already moaning.

Whoa, I'm pretty sure this is gonna be quick.

However, I cannot really tell my clients that because, obviously, I am not one hundred percent sure, and I do not want to get their hopes up. I can, however, give them the right perspective.

"Wow, girl! That's a hard one. Keep breathing and focus on blowing that pain down and out. That's it. That's perfect. Finish this one with a good, deep breath. There you go."

"Micah, I don't know. This is WAY harder than I remember. What's going on?"

"Shelby, these contractions are coming fast, and I believe your body is making lots of change and progress. Typically, when it's this intense right out of the gate it could mean you're gonna have a baby soon. Let's try some 'slow dancing' and see if we can't get your body to relax a little bit more."

Shelby agreed. Slow dancing is just like it sounds. The laboring mama puts her arms around someone's neck, then they proceed to sway slowly together. When the contraction comes the woman relaxes her legs and hips a little and sinks into the contraction while the partner supports her weight.

In this case, I would be Shelby's dance partner because her husband was having back problems. We began to sway, then her contraction kicked in. Shelby dropped her weight and lifted her feet up off the ground.

I'm sorry, WHAT? I am literally holding a pregnant woman.

I quickly flashed my shocked face to her husband. All I could do was shrug my shoulders and giggle. My client continued to trust me and lifted her feet with every contraction for the next half hour. I know, I know, you are very impressed.

During one of Shelby's contractions, she did not lift her feet but, instead, grabbed my face and said, "AAAAAAHHHHHH! OOOOOOOH! I don't know, Micah!"

"Shelby, it's okay. I'm right here. You're doing so good. You're having a baby, and everything is okay."

She seemed to receive my encouragement, then, BAM! Shelby began yelling and crying at the same time.

"Huh-huh-huh-huh, STOOOOP! AAAAARRRRGGGGGHHHH!"

Soon she was wailing and had a look on her face of terror!

"NO, NO, NO! Something isn't right. My back is killing me, and I feel like I'm gonna die! I feel so stupid and weak. What's happening?!"

"You are not weak! You're gonna get through this. Shelby, climb up on the bed. Get on your hands and knees so that I can massage your back. I know it's hard. I'm right here."

With tears, Shelby climbed on the bed on all fours. Her contraction started right away giving her no time to prepare. They were not even a minute apart.

"OH NO! NO! NO! AAAAAAAAAAHH!"

Shelby was now beating her fist into the bed and absolutely writhing! Her reaction was like none I have ever seen. She was shrieking through her tears. She was spending so much energy in this reaction; it was very clear she was beyond pain.

"UuuuuuuaaAAAAAAEEEEEeeeeh! STOOOOOP! AAAAAAAEEEEUUUUUH! NOOOOOOUUUUUH!"

I am running out of vowels for her, people.

She was absolutely out of control! It sounded like she was losing her mind, and I truly felt for her. I had to help turn this around for her. Like I said earlier, **I'M NOT INTO TORTURE!**

"Shelby, you're gonna have to try to slow down and catch your breath so you can gain a little bit more control. You ready? Breathe with me."

I led by example and took a big deep breath in through my nose. With her head buried in her hands, she nodded her head "yes," and I could hear her doing the same.

Then, without any inflection in her voice, she reported: "I need to push."

It was almost spooky the way she shifted so seamlessly. *Doctor Jekyll and Mr. Hyde, much?* However, it was perfect timing!

Shelby's labor and delivery from start to finish was only two hours long. **When a birth happens that fast, the intensity is like being in transition for those two hours. It is very hard to wrap your head around it.** Your mind is telling you that it is too soon for this kind of pain, and you are wondering why you already want an epidural. It is hard to get in the game and get your focus and control.

Shelby did a fabulous job, but after that experience, she changed her tune about having a fast birth. Her baby, on the other hand, was one of the calmest, coolest, and most collected babies I have ever seen. The nurses had already bathed him and weighed him, and he did not make a peep. When it was time for this alert, yet quiet, baby to get his shots, the nurse pulled out the needle and stuck it in the baby's leg. He blinked his eyes, turned his head, and stared at the nurse. Nothing. No yelp, no crying, no tears! What a little champ. *I don't think anything is gonna phase him. He must take after his daddy.* Now that I think about it, his daddy did not say a word during the birth. It all makes sense now.

It can be just as hard on a first-time mama to have a fast birth as it is to have a long, drawn out one. Lots of women come to realize that they would rather take the slow boat to China than a one-minute walk on hot coals with a boa constrictor wrapped around their neck all while dealing with a UTI.

flip the switch

I WILL TELL YOU what, most veteran mamas go into labor with more confidence than their first time around and are ready to kick labor's butt! So many of my repeat clients show up at the hospital between seven and nine centimeters dilated, and some crazy women are already at ten! For them, active labor looks like early labor. Their breathing is perfect, they are under control, and as I like to say, "managing their contractions beautifully!" Having had at least one baby puts them at an advantage, no doubt. If someone walked into the room, he or she might not even know my client was in labor at all. *Impressive!*

However, during birth, every woman gets to that point where, in an instant, everything

changes. Just like the nursery rhyme says, "Then along came a spider, and sat down beside her, and frightened Miss Muffet away!"

"Then along came transition, and knocked her on her ass, and frightened my client away!"

Y'all know I ain't lyin'!

Natalie was a young, uber-fit athletic coach and absolutely ready to tackle labor. She had music going and was dancing through her contractions. She was actually coaching herself.

"You got this, Nat... Stay focused and keep movin'. Here we go, let's tackle another one."

Natalie was walking around, swaying, and continued to stay relaxed and focused. For several hours she was chatting between contractions, even smiling.

Then transition came. This put together, confident, under control woman completely disappeared. It was like a different person appeared in the room.

"Hey! Y'all need to shut up!" Everyone stopped in their tracks, looked at Natalie, and did not say another word. "You're having way too much fun. What do you think I'm doing here?!"

Yes, ma'am. We're shifting gears, got it.

She got into the bed and was trying to find a comfortable position to manage her contractions. Let me just say, that was too lofty of a goal.

"Y'all are killin' me! Hurry up and figure this out! I'm about to have another one... Oh SHIT!"

Her husband, Jeremiah, was standing beside her and had his arm wrapped behind her back. She was leaning back on him, and this appeared to be working for the next five or six contractions. However, this six-foot-seven giant of a man was starting to get really uncomfortable. Poor Jeremiah, he was just shifting a little bit when...

"What are you doing? Are you moving? Babe, I need you to STOP moving!"

He stopped and remained in that position for another couple of minutes and then attempted again to alter his position slightly to get some relief.

"ARE YOU KIDDING ME? STOP IT JEREMIAH!"

I was pretty sure she was close to being complete and would start pushing soon. I looked over at the midwife and quietly asked if she was thinking the same thing.

"SHHHH! YOU GUYS... SERIOUSLY!"

I looked at the midwife again and made a "whoops, my bad" kind-of face. Her face turned bright red as she was trying to keep it together so as not to disturb Nat. "CAN Y'ALL PLEASE DO SOMETHING? DO YOUR JOBS!"

It's showtime.

I finally spoke up. "Hey, Nat, you're absolutely in the zone! Are you feeling any pressure in your bottom?"

"Micah, I'm feelin' all kinds of stuff in my bottom. Now, WHAT'S THE PLAN?!"

"Let's see if you're complete so we can start pushing."

"There you go. Now that's helpful. Come on, come on, LET'S GO! What's takin' so long!"

Sure enough, she was ten centimeters dilated; it was time to deliver this baby.

And that's how it's done.

How about Leslie? This client was unique from the start because she had done her research and was desiring to have a pain-free birth. **Now,**

before you start judging, I will say that it is very possible to go through LOTS of hard work but not consider it pain. There are books and articles out there that talk about the kind of mindset one must have to prepare for this kind of experience. It is all very interesting, and looking back, I would say that a few of my birth experiences would fit into this category. They were VERY hard, but not what I would consider the "most pain I've ever been in."

So, as Leslie's doula, I was all for her going for this! We had many conversations, and we were on the same page as to how to achieve this goal.

It was "birth" day, and Leslie was absolutely rocking labor. She was walking around and breathing with no effort at all. She was carrying on conversations and looking great!

Several hours had gone by, and I remember Leslie saying, "I just don't understand what's happening, Micah. There just doesn't seem to be anything really going on. I'm not hurting, it's not hard. I'm concerned I'm not as far along as I think I am. We're just waiting around."

"Remember, this is the type of birth you were goin' for. You wanted a "pain-free" experience and that's what you should continue to expect and try for."

"You're so right. I'm just surprised I guess. I'll just continue on this course until I see my baby."

Leslie continued for about half an hour with no trouble at all. She was walking and swaying, then she leaned over onto the bed. She took a deep breath as another contraction started, swayed her hips, then exhaled long and slow. *Perfect!*

She took another deep breath, then, "I don't - want - TO DOOOO THIS ANY- more!!!"

Where did that come from?

Mid-sentence, this loud cry of exhaustion echoed throughout the room. "I want the meds!"

"You got it."

Pain medication through an IV works immediately. It does not completely remove the pain, but it takes the edge off and makes you not care. It is like the best margarita you have ever had. *Yes, please.*

After only a few minutes after the medication had kicked in, Leslie looked up and said, "I feel like a person again."

"I'm so glad. Let's just keep breathing through these contractions and in no time, you'll see that..."

"I need to poop."

See, no time at all. *Y'all catchin' on?* She did not really need the medication, but it helped her to gain her composure and finish the job. Time to push.

This next client, Lydia, already had two older children, sixteen and twenty, from a previous marriage. She was now pregnant again at the age of forty. Her goal was to have a positive birth experience, and giving birth naturally was the way she wanted to go.

Can I just take a minute to brag on my "late in life" preggos? **I have had many clients over the age of forty, and they are absolute ROCKSTARS!** I do not know if it is life experiences that enable them to cope so beautifully with birth but, generally speaking, they make these twenty-year-olds look like little girls. *Don't be mad young'uns.* Let me brag because there are very few things that us "older women" feel like we can do better than our younger counterparts.

Back to Lydia and her amazing birth story. For

most of her labor, she sat on the birthing ball with headphones on her ears. She was practicing the Hypno-Birthing method and listening to prerecorded inspirational messages to help her focus. Honestly, I had never done so little at a birth up to this point. For most of the time, I sat in a rocking chair, relaxing, and just watching my client. There had been no complaining from her, and she was not even doing any significant breathing. Her eyes were closed, and she was slowly circling her hips on the ball. It was peaceful and tranquil.

A few hours went by, and, after one of her contractions, she pulled out her earplugs, opened her eyes, and said, "I want an epidural."

Did I miss something? I haven't heard a peep out of you.

"Lydia, you're doing so good. What's up?"

She smiled at me and with a calm, cool voice and said, "I'm just at the end, and I can't do this anymore."

That was unexpected; talk about "flipping the switch." The nurse came in and checked her, and, sure enough, she was at ten centimeters.

Of course, she is. "Eighty-six the epidural." You go, girl.

June was a three-peat client. She was definitely a "pro" at giving birth. She did a great job at her first and second births but her third birth was absolutely inspiring. She invited two of her friends to be part of the experience, and she showed them how to get it done. She was talking and laughing with them for most of labor. It felt like a party, not childbirth.

I was using this birth as a training birth for one of my apprentices. Becky would be taking the role as the lead doula, but there was not really anything to do so far. We all had gotten pretty comfortable as June continued breezing through contractions.

After only about an hour of being at the hospital, June finally spoke up.

"Okay, you guys. It's starting to get a little harder."

Not a lot of movement from anyone, and I was intentionally taking a "back seat" to allow my apprentice to take some initiative, which she did.

"You are doing so good, June!"

Another contraction hit, and we could see June breathing through it, but still so effortlessly.

"Alright, I need some coaching."

This comment was directed to Becky and June's husband, George. They remained seated and both affirmed her breathing and how relaxed she was.

I knew this client very well, and I could see things were starting to escalate for her. Her face grew a little sterner, she was taking deeper breaths, and she began shifting her body to find some relief.

It was obvious to me that what was working was no longer helping her anymore. Her change was ever so slight, and I think that is why Becky and George did not recognize it right away.

I decided to stand up and, hopefully, encourage the two of them to see what I was seeing and take a little more action.

June repeated her statement. "Hey, guys. I'm needing something!"

I was actually very proud of June for speaking up and letting the room know that she was in need. Even though I was the mentor doula at this birth, I decided to move towards the foot of June's bed.

As I did, she lunged forward and grabbed my shirt. She literally pulled me into the bed, so I was on top of her and bracing myself against the bed rails so that I did not fall on her with all of my body weight. June had snapped and was now undone!

"SOMEBODY NEEDS TO DO SOMETHING NOW!!"

Everybody jumped to their feet, but it was too late. She had a death grip on me and, with crazy wide eyes, yelled right in my face!

"I NEED SOME HELP! HELP MEEEEEAAAAAHH!!! THIS BABY IS COMIN'! UUUUUOOOOAAAAH!"

One contraction, one push, Baby was here! I do not think she let go of me until they asked her if she wanted to hold her baby.

She loosened her grip.

I looked into her eyes and shared my thoughts. "Well, that was quite a ride! Was it good for you?"

"I need a drink."

Cue baby in arms.

It can be so entertaining to see a picture-perfect mama minding her own business, then that old spider "comes up beside her," takes a bite, and releases a venom that turns her into Medusa.

It is rewarding and fun working with these pros, but, as you can see, they are not exempt from dealing with the difficulties of childbirth.

too easy

*N*OW, FOR ANY OF us who have had babies, can we all admit that the first birth was a doozie? **We all start as amateurs, and we just don't know what we don't know.** At times, it is an unnerving process, and we are looking for the end probably way sooner than we should be. Having said that, every once in a while, I get some first timers that seem to give birth effortlessly. They make birth look WAAAAAY too easy.

Kathy and her husband, Jimmy, were a sweet young couple who apparently had life on a silver platter. I know that there is no perfect couple, but these two seemed to have everything going for them. They were smart, attractive, and had many friends. Jimmy had the perfect job, and Kathy was super creative with her time and resources. They were best friends, and I never, and I mean never, saw them in distress. I'm not going to lie, this concerned me a little. Would she have what it took when labor started to get hard? Did she even know what hard meant?

Kathy was thirty-eight weeks pregnant, and I got a text from her saying she was headed to the hospital. Over the past few hours, she had been having some contractions that were increasing in intensity, and she wanted to see what was going on. When I arrived, she was in the bed getting her vitals taken and her IV put in while Baby was being monitored. She was all smiles, and her voice was as pleasant as could be. Every three to four minutes, she would stop talking for about ten seconds, then would look at us and continue the conversation. Are you thinking what I'm thinking? She got to the hospital waaaaay too soon. *This may be a while.*

It was very busy on the Labor and Delivery floor that day, so Kathy had not had an exam yet. After about thirty minutes, the nurse came back in to check Kathy's dilation, and she was already at six centimeters. *Well, alright.* Kathy was thrilled, and I told her to continue relaxing and enjoying the experience. The next contraction came, and it was the first time Kathy made any noise at all.

"Whoa! I could really feel that one."

Wait, that's it? That's all you got for me?

"Good, Kathy. Can you explain how it felt different?"

"It was tighter, and I feel like I need to use the restroom all of a sudden."

Hmmmm… It was not really time for that; the nurse had just checked her. Not even a minute later another contraction came.

"Uuuuuuh. Hey, guys, I really need to go to the bathroom."

My spidey-senses were tingling.

"Sounds good, I'll let the nurse know."

There was no time for that; she was having another one.

"Uuuuuuuuuuh. Whew. UUUUUUh."

I pulled back the covers to help her get out of bed, and what did I see? A baby's head crowning, that's what! *Are you kidding me?*

"Jimmy, push the nurse call button. Kathy, your baby is coming. Stay right where you are."

"My WHAT?!"

"Yes ma'am. Somebody's in a hurry."

We heard a voice over the intercom. "Can I help you?"

"We need some help here. Baby is coming."

"I just checked her not even five minutes ago. I'm sure it's not Baby. I'll be back there in a little bit."

"Excuse me, I'm not interested in catching a baby today. I can see the head. We need some help here. Thank you SOOO much!" *Y'all feelin' me?*

The door flew open, and the nurse walked straight to the computer.

Pretty sure you won't find a vagina there.

She typed in a few things that, I am sure, were earth-shattering, then grabbed her gloves. As she was putting them on, she started walking toward Kathy.

"Oh my goodness! We need the doctor! You're about to have a baby!"

WOW! Now that was an inspired revelation.

"Kathy, I need you to stop pushing. We need to wait for the doctor to get here."

First of all, how could she wait for the doctor? Secondly, she had not been pushing. This baby was coming all on his own! And lastly... *oh, hello baby!*

How about Betsy? This first-time mama arrived at the hospital and immediately said she wanted some analgesic medication through her IV drip. I have never had a client do that before or since. She climbed in the bed, got her medication, and said she wanted to get some rest. At that point, all I knew was that she was more than three centimeters dilated because they would not have admitted her to the hospital otherwise. It was evident that this mama would probably not make it to the end without an epidural.

After about thirty minutes of sleeping, Betsy woke up and said, "Can you please call the nurse and tell her to bring me some more meds?"

Say what?

"Betsy, do you want to go to the bathroom first before she gives you some more?"

Now, this was a ploy. I did not care if she needed to pee. I was trying to get her out of the bed and get her moving. **She was going to be laboring FOREVER if she stayed in that bed.**

"No. I'm just too tired to get out of bed."

She pushed the nurses' call button. *I think she was on to me already.* The nurse came in, took her vitals, then gave her another dose.

Y'all, my client was snoring! I have never seen a woman sleep this hard during labor under analgesics.

Another thirty minutes went by, and I was trying to come up with a plan B. I talked to the nurse whom I have worked with many times before. I decided to do something I don't usually do. I told her that I would like for Betsy to have a vaginal exam just so I could use those stats to help motivate her to get moving. I wanted to show her that she was not going to progress very much while lying in the bed. The nurse agreed.

"Betsy, can you hear me? How are you feeling?"

"I'm just so sleepy. All I want to do is sleep."

"Okay. Well, we want to do an exam real quick and see what kind of progress you're making. Sound good?"

"Sure." Yawn.

What am I doing here?

The nurse checked Betsy's cervix and looked at me before she announced the results. "Well Betsy, you're complete."

Oh, come on! Sleeping through labor?! Women do not sleep through labor on simple pain medication.

Now how will I keep her awake enough to push?

Occasionally, I have close friends that hire me to be their doula. Shelly was one such friend. She had encountered some bad experiences with miscarriages and a terrible first birth full of interventions and medications. I wanted to do anything I could to support her. I received a text from her saying she was headed to the hospital after we had been communicating about her labor for a couple of hours. I typically get another update within twenty to thirty minutes of my client arriving in triage, which is about how long it takes to get monitored and receive a vaginal exam. It had now been an hour, and I had not heard from her.

Uh-oh, I think she's chickened out from even trying to have a natural birth.

I jumped in my car and headed to the hospital. When I got to the room, she was walking around, and the anesthesiologist was already there getting everything ready to administer an epidural.

"Hey, girl."

"Micah. You're here!"

"You OK?"

"I just don't know what to do. It's happening so fast!" She was pacing and seemed tense.

The midwife looked at me and said, "She's an 8, Micah."

What are you thinking, girl? You're almost done!

She started to have another contraction, and I noticed she was breathing effectively and managing the intensity nicely.

"Shelly, that was perfect!"

Meanwhile, the anesthesiologist was waiting for Shelly to get on the bed, and spoke up, "Now, you're gonna need to sit up on the bed and be very still for this. You can't move."

"What? I'm not going to be able to sit still! That's impossible!"

Y'all, Shelly was basically running from the anesthesiologist.

"I can't do this. How am I supposed to sit still? Wait. Do I need an epidural?"

Wait. Come again?

She was genuinely asking the midwife and me if she needed an epidural. *Let me think... Umm, hmmm? NOPE.*

"I don't think you need one", I responded quickly.

"You don't have to get an epidural."

Shelly looked up at the ceiling and pondered for about five seconds, then said, "Yeah, I don't think I want one."

That was an easy sell.

This was very unusual. Once a mama decides to get an epidural, it means she is done. She does not rethink or overthink. She does not reassess, *Hmm, do I need an epidural? Like, hmm, do I need a piece of pie today? You know, I don't think so. I changed my mind, I'm gonna exercise some self-control.*

The midwife suggested that Shelly get another exam. She was at ten centimeters. *Of course, she was.*

I was having lunch with Helen and her husband, Isaac, for our second and final prenatal meeting.

A quick sidebar, Your Honor?

In my doula practice, clients attend an initial "Meet & Greet" interview, a client class, and a final prenatal meeting. The first meeting is to listen and get to know these potential clients. We talk about what a doula is, how I can support them, and answer any other questions they may have. The client class is filled with information, scenarios, and practical hands-on training. Our final meeting is to talk very specifically about their birth wishes and any other situations that may have arisen during her pregnancy. While I think it is important to build a strong relationship with my clients throughout their pregnancy journey, I like to keep things simple when it comes to anything prenatal. I am glad my clients can ask me questions and I can offer advice, especially first-time moms. **I also think it is important to remind them that their doctors or midwives are the main caregivers during their pregnancy and any medical help they need**

should come from them. My clients value my primary role taking place on Game Day, and when mama goes into labor, I am there to give her the support she needs.

So, back to lunch with Helen. Her due date was about six weeks out, and we discussed the things she could be doing between now and then to help her in labor and delivery (things like uterine support, cervix softening, and perineal massage). *What do we call that? All together now class: SEX. That's right.*

I answered a few questions, and she seemed prepared and eager to have her baby. Maybe too eager.

Around five that night, I got a phone call from Isaac.

"Hey, Micah, how are you?"

"I'm good, Isaac. Did you guys have another question?"

"Yep. We're wondering if we should go to the hospital."

Okay, y'all. Did you listen to a word I said today?

Helen was probably experiencing Braxton Hicks. Braxton Hicks contractions are not real birth contractions. True contractions need to be at least five minutes apart and significantly stronger than just cramping. My advice to concerned moms is to **stay home as long as you can during early labor.** *Maybe just seeing me got her over-thinking about the birth.*

"Oh wow, what's goin' on?"

"Well, we got home, and Helen went to the restroom. She saw a little blood and got concerned. I told her to lie down, and we'd call the doctor if she wanted me to. She didn't seem to care one way or the other and has been resting for about an hour. She woke up feeling crampy."

I knew it. **Cramping and a little spotting will spook a first-time mama every time.**

"That's pretty normal and nothing to be too concerned about. If the spotting turns into bleeding then, yes, give your doctor a call. I agree with you that resting is probably the best thing for now."

"Yes ma'am, but since about 4 p.m., she's been having consistent contraction-type sensations. They're getting closer together, and I'm thinking we should go in. She says it's too early though."

Ooooooh, I see. This dad was getting nervous.

"Got it, Isaac. Would it be possible for me to talk to Helen myself? It might give me a better picture of what's goin' on."

"Yes! That would be great! Thank you!"

I was about to get the real scoop of how far along she actually was.

"Hey, Micah." Helen was panting as if she had been running for an hour.

"Hey, girl. Tell me what's goin' on?"

"Well, I told Isaac that I'm really starting to feel these contractions, but I know it's just too soon to go in."

Atta girl.

"Got it. And he said it's been about an hour of that?"

"Hang on." I heard Helen take a deep breath, then, "Ooooooooohhh, MMMMMMMMMM, aaaaaaaahhhh!"

Rinse and repeat four more times. That contraction was a minute and a half long!

"Great job, Helen. How long have you been breathing like that?"

"OOOOOOOOO! AAAAAAHHH! I'm not suuure - ooooooooooh! AAAAAAAAHHHH!!"

Ummmmm, yeah.

"Let me talk to Isaac, Helen." I could still hear her in the background.

"Isaac, I'm hesitant to say this because this is Helen's first baby, but she sounds pretty far along. Now, you know your wife and what her pain tolerance is. What's your gut feeling?"

"I can tell she's really having to focus, and it seems very intense. I've never seen her like this, but she's right. It does seem too soon."

"Isaac, I need you," Helen yelled from the other room.

"Y'all need to head to the hospital right away, and I'll meet you guys there."

"Are you sure?"

"Pretty darn."

I walked in the doors of the Labor and Delivery floor, and the nurse greeted me with, "Better hurry. She's a nine."

And that explained a lot! I walked into the room, and she had a deer in the headlights look about her.

"Wow, Helen! I'm impressed! That was so fast! How are you doin'?"

"I think I'm okay."

For the next forty-five minutes, I helped Helen with her breathing while her body seemed to be stuck at nine centimeters. This is NO BUENO! We are not designed to be in transition that long. Baby seemed to be lined up perfectly, there was no anterior lip in the way, and she was definitely in control. **This had to be mental.** She was still six weeks away, and I just saw them a few hours ago talking about all the things she should be doing to prepare.

"Helen, can you look at me for a sec?"

She turned and looked intently into my eyes. She was getting tired and maybe even a little discouraged.

"What are you thinkin' about? Where's your head right now?"

This is a question I reserve only for these types of moments. Helen seemed a little bit lost and aimless.

"I'm not sure, Micah. It's just not happening like I thought it would."

You are having every woman's dream birth, girl.

"So, are you ready to have this baby, Helen?"

"No. Not really. I thought I had another six weeks."

Helen breathed through another very hard and long contraction. I quickly affirmed her and then addressed what I thought the issue might be.

"I completely get that. That's no problem. It looks like your body is just waiting on you to get mentally ready. That's totally fine. We can wait as long as you need to. We'll just keep breathing through some more contractions, then you let us know when you're ready."

I think by now y'all have me figured out. I was setting the trap and waiting for her to take the bait. Another contraction came and it was a big one.

"Take a good deep breath in, then blow it out long and slow."

"Pppsssshhhh… wwwhhhheeeeeeehhhhh… I'M READY TO HAVE THIS BABY! I CAN'T DO THIS ANYMORE! AAAAAAAHHHHHH"

Gotcha.

Baby was born in five minutes.

That's it? That's all it took? You just had to decide you were ready?

Wow, that was just too easy!

Some women are just granted the ability to have easy births. They make it look ever so simple and beautiful. There is no point in aspiring to be them. They cannot help it. They were born to give birth. These women are not to be judged or envied... they are to be plagiarized. Let's all steal their birth stories! *Who's with me?!*

CHAPTER 11

midwives and doctors and nurses, oh my!

*M*ANY OF THE AMUSING moments that my clients and I have looked back on have involved some of the medical staff in attendance during birth. Of course, birthing professionals are very important to a woman's experience during childbirth. I have worked with some wonderful caregivers, and my encounters have been mostly positive. This does not mean, however, that it has all been perfect and exactly how my client would have wanted it. Still, they have been positive experiences overall. Here are just a few entertaining situations with the midwives, the doctors, and the nurses.

Midwives

I have actually had three different midwives myself and have worked with about eight to ten different ones over the years. I love midwives! If you have heard anything about them, you might think that they are all relatively the same. **Most people have a certain stereotype in mind when they hear the word, "midwife."** However, their training and personalities create a "scale of extremes," you might say, and I have encountered the whole spectrum.

My first personal experience with a midwife was more on the Mother-Earth, crunchy, "vaginas are beautiful" end.

She would say things like, "Micah, you have the best birthing pelvis and hips I've ever seen."

Thanks? Not what every twenty-one-year-old is looking to hear.

Then, during our childbirth education class, she had us go through a visualization exercise.

"During this contraction, picture a flower opening up and blooming. Not a red flower but a blue flower that is cooling your perineum. Allow the nectar to lubricate so that Baby can slip and slide down into the birthing canal. Can you see it? Can you feel it? Can you smell it?"

I'm trying not to.

While at a routine appointment, she laid down on the bed with me, breastfed her baby, and gave me a vaginal exam all at the same time. We were just all in it together. It definitely had that "village" feel, and it made everything feel very natural and even normal. *We're just havin' a baby here. No biggie.*

Some midwives have a different approach; a bit more clinical. They might practice in a birthing center or in a hospital, full scrubs, a stethoscope around their neck at all times, and charting every twenty minutes. They could also be at your home birth fully equipped with the drugs, the mask and gloves, and an oxygen tank. There would be no need to purchase supplies like gauze or chucks pads, or sterilize the blankets and towels in the oven, not be opened until birth. *Yes, that's a thing.*

I have seen midwives do some incredible things. I have seen them deliver a baby whose shoulder was stuck (Shoulder Dystocia) and witness them turn a baby in utero to perfectly line up for delivery.

One time, a laboring mom chose "flight" instead of "fight" and was trying to climb up the headboard of her bed (because that will make the pain go away, right?) with a bulging water bag hanging between her legs. The midwife calmly crawled onto the bed, grabbed the water bag with one hand, and popped it. She very sweetly said, "Here's your baby." The mom immediately squatted to look down and when she did, that head came flying out! The midwife was right there to catch the baby. She told this mama to grab hold of her shoulders for balance and to sit down right where she was. She placed the baby in mama's arms and hugged them both. *Simply amazing!*

The most amazing and, also, craziest thing I have ever seen a midwife do was for my own daughter, Gabrielle. She was going through labor beautifully, and I was so proud of her. I got to be there, and I had communicated in advance to our midwife, Kari, that I was still unsure of what my exact role might look like. Would I be in full doula mode, or resort to being a loving, supporting mom? Kari was an amazing support for both of us.

When it came time for transition, this big old chunky boy Gabrielle was delivering was having a hard time getting lined up correctly. With each contraction, she would squat while holding onto the hospital bed. This was just what her body was telling her to do.

Kari offered some guidance. "Gabrielle, I think the baby is slightly looking to the left. You may also have a little cervical lip. I'd like to try and move it out of the way for Baby to come on down."

"Sounds great! Do what you gotta do, but I cannot move from this spot."

Another contraction started and Gabrielle deep squatted to the floor.

"No problem. Keep doing what you're doing."

Kari proceeded to crawl under the hospital bed (you heard me) then inched her way towards Gabrielle. She calmly inserted her fingers and applied pressure to the cervical lip. *Y'all, I can't.*

"Now push, Gabrielle!"

"HUUAAAUUUH! THAAAT HUUURTS!"

It was obvious this is painful, and I wanted my daughter to know she was not alone.

"I know, sweet girl. I'm right here beside you. Listen to Kari so you can have this baby."

"OOOOOOOOOAAAAAAAAAAAAAAAH! I CAN'T MAMA!"

Kari yelled from under the bed. "I got it! You did it, Gabrielle!"

Kari quickly slid out from under the bed and started giving instructions to the nurses while she got her gloves on.

"I CAN FEEL SOMETHING! WHAT'S HAPPENING!"

I knew what that meant. As a doula, I was pumped and, as her mom, elated!

"That's your baby! Come on babe... PUSH!"

The next two contractions were fierce, but my sweet, strong girl did not shy away. That nine-and-a-half-pound baby was born within ten minutes of Kari getting down and dirty to help my girl. If you're reading this, Kari Herman... shout out to you! Luv ya!

Doctors

Now, you may think that doctors are not really all that funny. They are mostly serious, and for good reason; however, most of them do have a sense of humor.

Dr. Risotto is one of my favorite OB/GYNs. She is calm, confident, and she listens to her patients. Her thought is, if you and baby are doing well, then she does not really care what you do or do not do. **It is your birth. Do YOU.**

One day, we were working together at a birth and this one particular mama was having a hard time pushing her baby down into the birthing canal. We were a long way from the head crowning. There are a few tricks that I can pull out if a woman cannot naturally find her Sweet Spot when it comes to pushing. Dr. Risotto had her favorite go-to as well.

"Okay Micah, tie a knot on one end of this sheet and let Riley hold onto that end. Then you grab the other end and play tug-of-war with her."

I got the sheet ready and gave it to Riley.

"Now Riley, when you feel the contraction coming on, I want you to bear down, then pull against the tension and try to pull Micah in the bed."

"Got it. Here it comes."

Riley started to pull, and I provided the tension. Dr. Risotto was observing and semi-coaching. When the contraction was over, she took the sheet from Riley and faced me.

"Micah, you've gotta really pull."

She demonstrated and jerked the sheet very hard. Hello! I was not ready for that. I immediately stumbled forward right into Dr. Risotto. She fell backward, but thankfully a nurse was behind her and broke her fall. I was not so lucky. THUD! I'm good.

I jumped back up to my feet as quickly as I fell to the floor.

I flashed Dr. Risotto a big smile with wild eyes. "Are you SURE you want ME to play tug-of-war with the laboring patient in the hospital bed?"

The entire room of people, including my client, burst into laughter. Dr. Risotto was so caught off guard that she could not compose herself quickly enough for the next contraction. Maybe it was the laughter, maybe it was the release of tension, but that baby's head was pushing forward with each chuckle my client made. *Okay, now add physical comedy to my bag of tricks.*

The nurse began to coach the patient, then I chimed in with the "atta-girls" and other encouragement.

Dr. Risotto was still giggling as she placed her hands in a position to guide the baby's head.

"Alright now, here we go. Let's get focused," she said to herself.

We were all still smiling and making eyes at each other, but the doctor just could not get it together.

"I'm so sorry. I just cannot get that image out of my head! Micah! The shock, the stumble, the response, the grin, I'm dying over here!"

She could not contain herself. To her credit, she was in a position to catch this baby, she was just still laughing uncontrollably.

The nurse gave another instruction as the next contraction was coming. "Here we go, fill those lungs and push!"

"HUUAAAAAH! AAAAAAAAAAAH!"

Dr. Risotto tried to speak clearly through her chuckles. "Baby is com-hoohoa-haoo-mmming! Again, I'm so sorry ha-ha-haaaa!"

I tried to keep Riley focused. "One more good push, girl. Here we go!"

"WHAAAAAAAAAAAAAAAAAAAAAAAH! UUUUUUUUUUH!"

Dr. Risotto caught the baby and immediately passed him to his mama. She took a few steps back to gather herself as she was still laughing.

I was smiling from ear to ear. "He's here! You did it! I'm so stinkin' proud of you!" Yes, I was still amused, but I was mostly feeling pride. My clients and their strength inspire me and my celebration of them and their accomplishments is genuine.

"Oh my gosh! I can't believe it! That was amazing! Thanks, everybody! I never thought I would laugh a baby out!"

That makes six of us.

There was one anesthesiologist that had quite the reputation.

One of my clients, Dani, asked for an epidural, and the nurse rolled her eyes when she said his name.

"Okay. We'll get the order put in right away. It's gonna be Dr. Cootie that's on-call today."

Cue smirks. It took about twenty minutes for him to get to my client's room. The door swung open as wide as it would go and banged up against the wall. He pushed his stainless steel, squeaky wheel cart while he clumsily kicked it with each step he took. He then proceeded to run into the very large and obvious rocking chair before introducing himself.

"YEP! I'm sure you ALREADY guessed it... I am Dr. Cootie! You doin' OK? What's your name?"

The nurse responded to Dr. Cootie with a whisper. "Dr. Cootie. This is Dani Weller and her husband, Jody."

Good thinking. Maybe he would catch on that he was too loud.

"I'm sorry? WHO'S Dani?"

"The patient's name is Dani Weller."

"Okay. Well, I see you've got your 'adoolah,' Micah."

I rolled my eyes, then turned and offered a fake smile. *It's "DOULA."*

He went over the procedure and asked a ton of questions, which, by the way, had already been asked and charted. Dani looked over at me with wide eyes.

She shook her head in disbelief. This was terribly distracting!

Push pause. Have you ever noticed that when you get to the hospital, they ask all the same questions that you filled out for pre-registration? With each procedure or medication given, they ask the same questions again and again. New nurse, the surgical team, the recovery room, postpartum wing, same questions... it does not seem to matter. No one knows how to read apparently. *Such a waste of time!*

Okay, rant over.

As he was preparing his station, every move was forceful and noisy. He slammed the scissors back on his tray, then tossed the empty vials into his plastic container.

Dani started to have a contraction, and I began to coach.

"You've got this, Dani. Just focus on your breathing. Tune everything else out." *Good luck and "may the force be with you."*

Dani took a deep breath and started to let it out slowly.

Dr. Cootie turned to the nurse. "OKAY! Uhhhh, what's her name?"

The nurse repeated her name again.

"Okay. Dani? Right?"

I responded by nodding my head yes.

"ALRIGHTY. Let's get this SHOW on the road! You gotta SIT UP, Darlin."

Jody stepped forward to shake Dr. Cootie's hand. "Excuse me, sir. I'm Jody, Dani's husband. I think she's in the middle of a contraction. Could you wait just a minute?"

Dr. Cootie stopped talking but continued his tasks. He opened the back of her gown and sprayed a cold antiseptic on her back. She winced but remained focused. He started pushing on her back, then continued his conversation with Jody.

"So, Dani, what do you do?"

"I'm sorry?" Jody was confused. The doctor was looking at HIM.

Too slow, Jody.

Dr. Cootie turned to Dani and continued speaking. "Well, I'm READY to administer the numbing meds. You ready now, Jody?"

I looked over at Dr. Cootie and held up my finger... nope, still not that finger. I was hoping to slow him down a bit.

Dr. Cootie stopped what he was doing and cleared his throat loudly, then looked back over to the only other male in the room.

"These women gotta have it their way, right, Dani?"

Good grief. As if the lack of personal awareness was not enough, he was calling all of us the wrong names.

The contraction ended, and Dani responded to Dr. Cootie. "Excuse me, SIR! Can you please be a little more patient? I need WAY less talking."

"You BET, Jody!"

Dr. Cootie whipped out the needle and gave the play-by-play of his every move.

"I am LOOKING for the right SPOT. AAH, TOUCHDOWN! I'm now inserting the NEEDLE! BIG STICK and a BURN..."

What is happening?

He turned back to his working area and continued with all the loud handling of everything he touched. He opened and slammed drawers and with each movement the metal cart shifted and squeaked.

The nurse and I stared at each other knowing that there was nothing we could do. This was the way it was with him every time. His only saving grace was that he excelled at finding the right spot, giving the right dose, and making women loopy!

"ALMOST DONE. Ah, Jody? Can you feel THIS?" He pressed on Dani's back with the epidural tube.

"Nope. Can you hurry? I'm about to start another contraction."

I was standing right in front of Dani, and she leaned her head over on me while sitting hunched over a pillow. I decided to be super proactive and distract her with my voice rather than all of the unnecessary background noise.

"Big deep breath, and blow it out long and slow. WHHHHHHHH. Excellent. Let's do that again. Deep breath, and blow everything down and out. WHHHHHHHH. Perfect, Dani! You've got this. Again."

I continued these calm, rhythmic encouragements throughout the entire contraction. Dani was oblivious to Dr. Cootie's commentary about her narrow lumbar vertebrae and his question about pain. He continued to make as much noise as was humanly possible while he cleaned up his station and got ready to go.

He held up two fingers in front of my client's face. "Just ONE LAST STEP. Can you SEE ME? Can you HEAR ME?"

You're joking, right?

There was no response to this question.

He turned to shake Jody's hand. "DANI, good LUCK, and I'm SURE I will now be your wife's FAVORITE male!"

He gave Jody a goofy grandpa smile and proceeded to run his cart into the bathroom door as he walked out. SLAM!

Don't let the door hit ya' on the way out, buddy.

Remember my three-peat client, June? Well, at her second birth, her midwife was out of town and Dr. Dewley was the on-call OB/GYN who was known for having a very clinical approach. I was a little concerned, but I figured we would just do our "thang" and wait until the last possible second before we called him in to deliver the baby. Everything was going exactly how June wanted: few interruptions, no monitors, and no vaginal checks. Labor was progressing right on track, then June began talking about feeling more pressure. Our nurse happened to be in there when June announced she had to poop. *Let's go!*

"Okay. Let's do a quick check so we can see if you're complete before you start pushing."

"No. I don't really want to be checked. Let's give it a few more contractions to make sure I'm even reading my body correctly."

Atta girl.

"Okay. We just want to make sure we give the doctor plenty of time to get in here."

"Of course. You bet, Gwen." I reassured the nurse that we were not trying to have a baby without the doctor.

Gwen knew that June was a midwife client, so she had been very cooperative so far in allowing June to labor the way she wanted. Mom's and Baby's vitals had looked great during the entire process. Gwen went to check on another patient and said she would be right back.

I turned to speak with June to try and ascertain exactly how far along she was. "Okay, girl. Whatcha thinkin'? Is it time?"

"I think so, but I just want to try and let Baby come down in her own time before we call in the cavalry."

Perfect!

June had two contractions, and she just simply breathed through them. As soon as the third contraction started, she began to bear down.

"HMMMMMMMM. WHOOOOOOOOOOA!"

June turned around to get on her hands and knees, then began to push.

Alrighty. It was time for reinforcements because, why? That's right, **I DON'T DELIVER BABIES, y'all!**

I called for the nurse first.

The charge nurse, Rosie, came in because our nurse was still in another room. "Hey, Micah. Talk to me. What do y'all need?"

Here's the thing. I have worked very hard in my community to establish this kind of working relationship. I have done this intentionally because it benefits my clients greatly! These amazing nurses know me, trust me, and have come to rely on me as it relates to my clients and their care.

"She's starting to push and is hoping to deliver on her hands and knees."

"You know who's on call, right?"

"I do indeed. Can we get her to the point of no return before we call him in?"

"Yes. That'll work because he's actually on the floor. It won't take any time."

"Awesome! Okay, June. Rosie is gonna give a quick peek just to see if Baby is closer than we think."

"Okay, but hurry. I'm starting another contraction." June took a deep breath and began pushing.

Rosie leaned down to check it out and immediately said, "Stop pushing! Baby's head is right there! Micah, call for the doctor."

(You can insert your favorite response here to the instruction, "Don't Push." I like, "HAAYLL NO!")

I called for the doctor while Rosie turned to get some gloves on.

I reassured June. "Keep doing what your body is telling you to do. Don't worry about the doctor. Just focus. Rosie knows how to catch a baby, and she's right here ready to go if the doctor doesn't make it."

June backed off a little bit and was bearing down rather than giving a hard push. Rosie came back to the bed and was supporting June's perineum as well as Baby's head. Her contraction ended.

"It buuurns sooo BAAAD! Where is he? I need to push y'all!"

Another contraction started immediately and in walked Dr. Dewley. He nodded to me and June's husband.

"Hello everyone. I'm Dr. Dewley. What have we got here?"

He made a face when he realized he was staring at someone's rear-end.

"Baby is right here, Doctor, and I'm just providing a little support. Tell me when you're ready for me to clear out."

"Let me get my scrubs and stuff on. Can you guys turn her around onto her back?"

A very emphatic response came from June. "NO! I'm pushing NOW! HUUUUAAH WOOAH!"

"Okay, I'm ready, Rosie."

Rosie moved out of the way to reveal that Baby's head was born.

"OH WOW! It's all you. Here we go aaand CONGRATULATIONS!"

"Oh my goodness, y'all! That was so intense and so fast!" You could hear June's relief in her sigh and see it in her body language.

Dr. Dewley looked around the room. "Hey, that was my first time to ever deliver a baby this way. I did pretty well." He pointed to my client's rear-end as he was congratulating himself.

I helped June spin back around onto her side.

June looked at the doctor. "Hi! I'm June."

"Nice to meet you, June. I'm Dr. Dewley."

"How was it for you?"

"That was a first for me. Never delivered a baby with the mom in that position before."

Hmmmmmmmm. I am not sure I can give him credit for "delivering" just because his hands were there when Baby's body came flying out. Regardless, we let him believe it to keep him from realizing the conspiring that took place so that June could deliver on her hands and knees.

And the Oscar goes to June... for Best Actress in a Supporting Role.

Nurses

Throughout this book, I have shared a little here and there about nurses. If you do not already know this, listen up, because this is gold! **Your stay at the hospital is all about your relationship with the nurses. Make friends with them quickly and let them do their job.** If you give them a hard time and question their every move, just remember, they can make or break your experience. They answer to three separate entities. First and foremost, they work for the hospital. They are the ones who uphold all of the policies whether they agree with them completely or not. They also answer to your caregiver. Your doctor or midwife oversees your birth, but the nurses are actually responsible for your care. They also answer to you, of course. And, more than likely, you are not their only patient. They try to balance all the requests, preferences, and demands given to them from multiple patients at a time. **When you understand their role, then it**

is quite easy to see why they deserve your respect. Once they see that you deem them as a valuable part of your team, then you will find VERY cooperative and sympathetic nurses. Speech over, and you're welcome, my RN friends.

I have had many encounters with all different types of nurses. There are the laid-back nurses who hang out in your room, sit down, prop their feet up, and eat your snacks... *my favs!* Then there are nurses that dot every "i" and cross every "t" and measure and weigh and check every single time you tinkle. I have even had brand new nurses serve my clients; I mean like, it was their first day.

While one of my clients was getting her IV, the nurse butchered her arm and could never find her cervix... *ouch!* My client told one of these sweet little things that she needed to leave the room and never come back.

I have also had seasoned veterans that can tell you that you are in transition without an exam and deliver your baby as professionally as a doctor.

One of the coolest things I ever witnessed was with one of my favorite nurses, Brandy. My repeat client's labor was proceeding very quickly, and she had only just arrived at the hospital. She was not even "officially" checked in. She started to bear down just a little, and Baby's head was crowning. Brandy was on it. She did not mess with the computer or the paperwork. She did not even say, "Stop pushing."

My client's husband was parking the car, and I texted him to hurry.

Another contraction came, and she pushed that baby's head right out. Here is the cool part. The amniotic sac was still intact around the baby's head; his hair was floating around in what looked like a fishbowl. *So AMAZING!* Brandy and I were in awe and, honestly, did not want to move on.

The dad walked in just in time to say, "What the hell am I looking at?"

Most people are not into the cool, amazing, or never-seen-before when it comes to birth. I get it. We're weird.

One particular, and highly entertaining, story involved an older nurse. I had a client being induced, and she remained in good spirits for the entire birth. Her nurse's name was Wanda, and she was absolutely the sweetest thing! Wanda moved at a methodical pace and had an ongoing power struggle with the computer. My client was hooked up to the IV, blood pressure cuff, pulse oximeter, and of course, monitors.

Not the ideal situation, but we got this.

Right away, we saw what our biggest challenge was going to be: Wanda could not hear very well.

She was definitely aware of this because, after several times saying, "What honey?" she finally said, "I don't hear as clearly as I used to."

Awwww. AND I DON'T WANT TO YELL AT YOU, sweet Wanda.

We were several hours into labor, and this client has not progressed the way we would have liked. She had to continue to go up on the Pitocin dosage until she finally had had enough and asked for an epidural. *Don't blame ya, girl.* The epidural was in, and the anesthesiologist was waiting to see how mom and Baby responded. Immediately, mom's blood pressure dropped which caused Baby's heart rate to drop as well.

Wanda was trying to reason with the computer once again when the anesthesiologist called for her attention.

"Wanda. Wanda! WANDA!"

I had to tap her on the shoulder.

"What is it, dear?"

I pointed to the doctor, then looked over at my client who seemed to be fine.

"Oh, yes, doctor?"

"We need to get this mama on her side and increase her fluids."

"What? Can you say that a little slower? I just don't hear as well as I used to."

"HER BLOOD PRESSURE!"

He pointed to the monitor showing her blood pressure and Baby's heart rate. This was also where EVERYTHING else was stationed so the pointing was useless.

Wanda grabbed the thermometer. Once she got to my client, she realized that was the wrong thing. She jerked back suddenly and dropped the thermometer on my client's head.

"Oh goodness, sweetheart. I've done it now."

"No, no. I'm fine, Wanda."

My client was smiling, so I smiled back. **Always go with the positive flow that your client is projecting.**

"Wanda! Please. ASAP on the fluids!"

"Oh. Yes, sir. No problem."

Apparently, Wanda had accidentally stepped on the IV tubes when she came with the thermometer. As Wanda moved toward the IV pump, I assisted the doctor in turning the client onto her side away from the connections.

"OH OUCH, OUCH, OUCH! MY IV!"

The IV site was being yanked from her arm. I looked around to see what was happening.

"Wanda, you're on the IV. Wanda, you are steppin' on the tubes! WANDA!"

I had to physically move her off the chords. This took her away from her task again.

"Oh no, honey! What is it?"

"You are standing on her IV tubes."

"HUH?"

"Look at the TUBES! You're standing on them!"

"Oh MY! I'm so sorry, honey."

The doctor was very frantic and loud, but my client was actually laughing.

"This is like a comedy routine. You can't make this stuff up!"

Well, that was unexpected.

The doctor sounded a little more stern. "Wanda! You HAVE to get her those FLUIDS, now!"

I reached down and picked up all of the attached dangling lines. Wanda started pushing buttons. Thankfully, Baby's heart rate started coming back up. The fluids were pumping pretty quickly, and her blood pressure was stabilizing. The tension in the room calmed back down.

Wanda walked over to the bed, put her hands on my client's face, and smiled. "Well, that was exciting, wasn't it, dear?"

My client and I began laughing uncontrollably. Wanda's mishaps continued to occur, but it just did not seem to matter or change the lighthearted tone throughout birth. Even when my client started talking about pressure, then updated with, "I think I'm pushing," I still had to walk over to get Wanda's attention. I even made up a little song to the Beach Boys hit, "Help Me, Rhonda."

"Help me, Wanda, help, help me, Wanda. Help me, Wanda, help, help me, Wanda. Help me, Wanda, Yeah… Get her outta my bod!"

Showing my age again, but it's a classic y'all!

"Wanda. Come look." I pulled the sheet up a little and revealed that Baby's head was crowning.

"Well, good grief. We better call the doctor. I've caused enough trouble for one day."

She looked up at me and smiled, and I could not help but burst into laughter. Wanda was the perfect nurse for this client.

My client's baby was born in an atmosphere of joy, contentment, and laughter.

You gotta always find the silver lining, ladies.

CHAPTER 12

well, that's embarrassing

*W*HAT ABOUT YOUR BLUNDERS in the birthing room, O Great and Mighty Doula? There is no lack for those, I am afraid. You may be asking, why are you even there in the first place? What does your presence in the birthing room mean? **Well, for most births, it means I help to promote peace and confidence.** I am typically hired to support the laboring mom with various comfort measures. I am also there to answer hard questions and provide mental and emotional guidance when things get difficult. And yes, sometimes my presence brings entertainment and humor.

Now, I am sure there are some things that have happened to every doula, like knocking things over or breaking things, for instance. I have knocked over my large Thermos full of coffee, a nurse's tray with my client's vials of blood, a rocking chair (ouch), and, oddly enough, a client's mother. I have broken portable monitors, a blood pressure cuff from hell (that may or may not have been on purpose), and a thermostat set to eighty degrees (it was hell and not on purpose). I even broke a hospital bed by sitting on the foot of it after I unintentionally unlocked it. The head of the bed popped up with my client in it before the foot of the bed fell onto the floor with me in tow. If any doula says that nothing like this has happened to her, then I am calling B.S.! I can't be the only one!

One of my clients was in the middle of getting her epidural and was sitting on the bed facing me, leaning over a pillow while I helped stabilize and soothe her. The anesthesiologist was looking for the right spot to give her the numbing shot and reminded her several times not to move.

All of sudden, my heart sank. I started my period! Absolutely no question about it. *What the heck am I supposed to do?* At first, I was frozen, mostly because my client was also frozen, and I simply could not move.

I whispered to the nurse, who happened to be a friend, "Girl, I just started my period."

Jaw dropped, eyes bugged, slight chuckle. "You're kidding?"

That would be a no.

"As soon as he gives her the shot, can you slide in here real quick so I can run to the restroom?"

"Yep."

The shot was over, and the nurse and I began moving slowly and quickly all at the same time. (Yes, you're correct, that doesn't work.)

My client inquired. "What's happening? What are y'all doing?"

We stopped in our tracks.

"Nothing, just need to shift for a quick sec."

"Well don't."

Yep. Okay. Sure thing.

The doctor spoke. "Alright, hold still, here comes the needle for the epidural. You're doing great. Don't change a thing."

The nurse and I looked at each other, and I made a face that communicated that it was okay. My pants were black, and I was sure it was fine.

Finally, the epidural was over, and I tried to leave very discreetly. That did not work either.

"Micah, are you okay? What's happening? Do you leave once clients get epidurals?"

This was quite the conundrum. Of course, I do not leave my clients! What kind of doula do you think I am?! *Now what?*

"No, I'm not leaving. I just have to run to the bathroom real quick."

I went to my bag, grabbed it, and tried to head to the door one more time.

Then, my client's husband inquired. He apparently had no sisters growing up, or dated very much or, now that I think about it, paid much attention to his own wife.

"Why do you need your bag? I thought you were gonna be gone for just a minute? I don't know what to do at this point. Can you stay?"

Really? The gig was up.

"Okay, gang, pretty sure I just started my cycle. Gotta go check things out. Be right back."

The nurse then cracked up and swooped in to distract the couple from my departure. I will spare you the rest of the details. And yes, I went back and finished my job, thank you very much.

Okay, here is another good one. I was with my client, Delilah, and everything was starting off well. She got through triage easily, she had a successful IV attempt on the first try, and now her breathing was in a relaxed rhythm. My client and I had talked about moving and walking as part of her labor experience. Delilah was already hooked up to everything, so I immediately requested portable monitors. Delilah's nurse was not sure if we were allowed to use them, so she left the room to go check with someone else. A few minutes later, our nurse returned with another staff member named Cherry. As the two walked in, Cherry walked straight to the monitor and looked at the strip keeping track of Baby's heart rate.

"Baby looks great, and you're doing great. Let's get these things off of you so you can walk around."

It is such a relief when you get staff members who listen, are reasonable, and want to work with you. I let Cherry know right away of my appreciation.

"Perfect! Thanks so much, girl!"

Now, I have worked with a lot of nurses over the years, and I do not always remember all of their names or when or if I have worked with them before. It does not matter to me, though, I treat all of them the same. Even if I have not worked with them very much, I connect right away to put them at ease. It was obvious to me that Cherry had seniority over our other nurse. I wanted to make sure she felt comfortable with me.

Labor continued, and Delilah was up and about. To my surprise, Cherry came in and checked on us periodically. **I love it when the hospital staff recognizes that they have a patient who wants things to look a little different.**

I quietly spoke to Cherry. "So, listen, I'm thinking about getting her in the shower. Is that cool with you? Maybe you can just wrap up the hep-lock with a small trash bag or glove. I'm super thankful that you're in here helping us out."

"No problem at all. I want what's best for Delilah. I'll be back. Certainly appreciate what you do for our patients."

I extended out my arm for a fist bump. Cherry smirked and returned the gesture. *Awesome!*

Our nurse returned to wrap up the hep-lock, and we got Delilah into the shower. It worked like a charm. While she was in there, lots of progress happened, and, within about forty minutes, she was talking about pressure in her bottom. *That's what I like to hear.*

The nurse left the bathroom, and I helped Delilah to the potty and got her dried off. I could hear by the way she was moaning that we were super close to delivery.

Our nurse walked in with Cherry. "Delilah, let's get you in the bed and check to see if you're complete."

We helped her to the bed, and Cherry gave her an exam. "Yep. You're complete!"

Delilah looked at Cherry puzzled. "What does that mean?"

"It means you can start pushing. Baby is still a little high so let's see if you can bring him down with some strong pushes."

"I don't think I can."

I pushed back the hair that was in Delilah's face and said, "Hey, tell me what's goin' on? You're here at the home stretch."

"I'm so tired, Micah. I'm afraid I just don't have the energy to have this baby."

"Got it. I know how tired you are. It's been a long day, and you've worked so hard. Cherry, maybe we can let Baby 'labor down' a bit before she starts pushing. Whatcha think?" I said this with a wink and a smile.

"I'm sure that would be fine."

"Great!"

Cherry was sitting on a rolling stool at the end of the bed. I began to help Delilah rest and focus on her breathing while we allowed Baby to come down a bit more. We were trying to help her save some energy.

Well, that didn't take long!

After maybe three contractions, Delilah began making involuntary pushing sounds. *Ta-Da!*

"Look at you go! Right on target. Feeling more pressure?"

"Yep! Lots and lots of pressure!"

Cherry walked toward the bed and put on a glove to check for Baby's head. "Oh wow! Very good! You can definitely start pushing. Baby is right here."

I looked at our nurse and asked, "Shouldn't we go ahead and call for the doctor? I think this is gonna go pretty fast. Don't you, Cherry?"

There was a long awkward pause and Cherry said, "I AM the doctor."

I was speechless. I had no idea what to say or how to make it look less like the biggest oversight you could possibly have in this scenario.

Thankfully, the nurse spoke up to try and save me some embarrassment. "Isn't it great how involved she is, Micah?"

"Absolutely! I'm so sorry. I had no idea..." *Obviously, dork.* "I've just never seen a doctor so involved. How did I miss that?"

"No need for apologies, Micah. We all make mistakes. Let's have this baby."

Oh, good grief! I could hardly focus, but thankfully there was not much to do. Baby was born in about fifteen minutes. I played back all the conversations we had earlier that day. What did I say that could have come across as unprofessional or even disrespectful? Oh, I know, fist-bumps and winks, along with "girlfriend" and "thanks for helping us out." *I am never recovering from this one.*

How about this? I called my client by the wrong name her entire birth! Yes, I did. I probably said Sharon a hundred times.

When that baby was born, I congratulated the couple. "Congratulations, Sharon! You did it! So proud of you!"

"My name is Cecelia, and thank you."

I probably shouldn't get paid for this one.

Okay, here is the last one I will tell on this subject. I was at the hospital with my client, Jolene, and her husband, Smithy. It was a fairly typical birth, and she had been breathing perfectly through her contractions. She was sitting on the birthing ball and moving her hips around in a circle. Things were starting to pick up, and for the first time that day, Jolene started talking about the analgesic medication. She was not asking for them; she was just asking about them. Big difference!

"Hey, Micah. These have jumped up in intensity pretty quickly. Can you tell me about my options with pain meds?"

"You bet. You can take meds through your IV, and they'll work immediately. Now, the pain won't go completely away; you just won't care because you're gonna feel tired. It will wear off in about thirty to forty-five minutes, but then you can get back out of bed, and we'll proceed. An epidural, of course, is the numbing of the lower half of your body by injection in your back. You will remain in bed and get a catheter with that procedure. We can also jump in the shower and see if that provides some relief before we try the meds. Most clients say the hot water on their back or tummy is bliss. Want to try that first? I think you're doing fabulous, by the way!"

I was trying to distract her from getting the medication and wooing her to the shower. Yes, I AM that good.

"The shower sounds good. I'm just not sure I can stand very long."

"Not a problem. I can take care of that."

I started the water and got Jolene ready to get in. There was no shower chair in this bathroom, but I had a better idea.

I grabbed the birthing ball. "Okay girl, let's step into the shower, and just go ahead and keep sitting on the ball in here."

"Oh, that sounds good."

Jolene carefully sat down on the birthing ball, and I adjusted the shower head and temperature.

"How's that?"

"Oh wow. It's perfect. Thank you."

This was a great opportunity to get my client's spouse involved. It would not be hard for him to just sit in the bathroom while his wife was in the shower. The curtain would be partially opened so my client could know she was not alone.

"Alright, Smithy. Here's the rolling stool for you to sit on. Keep encouraging her and let me know if y'all need anything."

I stepped out of the bathroom and took a minute to catch up on my birthing notes and sip on my coffee. One of the newer nurses, Clara, was in there with me, and we started chatting.

After five minutes, I heard Smithy's voice.

"Um, Micah?"

I stopped talking to hear Smithy better.

"I think we've got a problem here."

I was on the other side of the room and began to get out of my chair. Just like that phrase in the Bible, "And suddenly..." I saw almost an inch of water in the room pouring out from under the bathroom door! *Are you kidding me?*

"Uh, yeah, Smithy. The problem is in here, too! Hang on."

The nurse started freaking out a little and, without thinking, started calling for help...to no one. "We need some help in here! Can somebody help us?"

Not sure how effective that's gonna be, Clara!

"Clara, use the intercom."

She pushed the red button, and this was what came out of her mouth: "Help! We need help in here! There's a major problem!"

Not the words I would have chosen.

"Tell them to bring lots of towels. Check that. Bring lots of blankets."

Clara repeated what I said, then I sloshed through the flood to get to the bathroom. Jolene was in the middle of a contraction, and I lunged for the shower handle to turn off the water. Then I had to wait for her contraction to end (**do not EVER interrupt a woman during a contraction!**) so that I could move the birthing ball OFF the shower drain. *OHHHHH. That's what that's for.*

I walked back out of the bathroom, and right outside of our room I heard another nurse say, "What the hell?"

Oh, good. You see the problem, too... out in the hall.

In walked two veteran nurses with two blankets apiece. One of them was the charge nurse and a long-time ally of mine. I was grateful to see her.

"What in the world is going on, Micah?"

"I flooded the bathroom and apparently the hallway, too."

"You did what? How?"

"Did you know that if you cover the shower drain with a birthing ball it will flood the room?"

They both started laughing as they looked around the room and saw the damage.

"Girl, they're never gonna let you come back."

"Oh, that's helpful."

At that point, all I could do was laugh with them. Meanwhile, someone was in the bathroom trying to have a baby. Jolene was on her hands and knees on the bathroom floor, in the water, pushing and making grunting sounds.

Oh, HAYYYLL no!

The nurses dropped the blankets, and the three of us carefully lifted and dragged her to the bed. This was not easy because we were trying not to slip.

The charge nurse called for all hands-on deck. "Please send everyone who is not in another room to room 380! Call housekeeping, and we need at least twenty towels and ten blankets!" Jolene was pushing and we could see Baby's head crowning. "Oh, and send the doctor right away!"

Let's see if you can imagine the absolute chaos going on. The rest of the staff on the Labor and Delivery floor entered the room. Everyone looked like they were in slow motion trying to maneuver in an inch of water. There was a baby coming! Right then!

"What were y'all doing?" inquired one of the new arrivals.

The charge nurse flashed a mischievous grin at me while she continued to assist Jolene. "It was Micah trying to show off all of her doula bag of tricks."

Now that was funny.

Enter the doctor.

"Careful Dr. Hank. Don't slip."

Dr. Hank looked at the floor, slowly crept in, and carefully lifted each leg high enough to cross the Atlantic. He looked around the room and then again at the floor.

"Should I even ask?"

I vote no.

"Doctor, Jolene is crowning, and Baby is coming."

"I'm coming as fast as I can. Jolene, how are we doing?"

"HHHHUUUUUAAAAAUUUUUHHHH!"

Well said, mama. And, not fast enough, doc!

"Okay, Jolene. I need you to stop pushing so I can get my gloves and gear on."

"SSHHHEEEEE'S COMIIIIING!"

Jolene was on her hands and knees. Despite the commotion, she was totally focused and about to have this baby whether we were ready or not.

"AAAAAAAAAUUUUUUUUH! MICAH!"

"That's it girl, big push. There's the head. Now one more for the body. You did it, Jolene! She's here!"

Jolene sat up on her knees, reached down, and pulled her baby up towards her. Instant delight set in for this strong mama who, on her own, just delivered her sweet baby. *Wow! Gotta luv it!*

The delivery room felt like a zoo. Seven nurses mopped up water, the charge nurse cleaned up Baby, Smithy was still stuck in the bathroom, and the doctor, who never got his gear on, turned right back around, said "Congrats," then tip-toed out the door.

They no longer let me operate the shower in that hospital.

As I said before, my clients and I are all in it together. **It is so healthy, and way more fun, for us to just laugh at ourselves and enjoy these blunders as they become part of our cherished birth memories.**

CHAPTER 13

yep! there's a man in the room

I THINK I HAVE only been to a few births where there was not a man in the room. Besides the doctor, this means more than likely, the dad. My husband, Michael, attended five births out of the six that I had (baby number six was an emergency C-section at twenty-seven weeks). Even though I always had great female support at my births, my memories of him are unforgettable. He has a quiet strength that I thrive on. He did not say much at any of our births, but when he spoke, I heard him above all others. The truth is, though, during most of the birth, he was probably reading his paper, doing a crossword puzzle, answering someone's trivia questions, or just observing me bringing our sweet baby into the world.

All this to say, my husband is calm, cool, and collected! He is NOT an alarmist, although, full disclosure, at times I may have wanted him to be.

Here are a few of the statements made by my husband in action:

"No, honey, I don't think that is a contraction. I think it's just gas."

"Okay great, we'll call Toni and tell her you're ready for her to come."

"Oh hey, Toni. This is Michael. Yes, she's wanting to push. Can you talk me through what I should be doing?"

"Micah, Connie needs to turn the baby. Just listen to my voice and follow what I'm saying."

"I know the head is born, but you're gonna have to push the shoulders out. You've got this, babe."

Michael "showed-up" when he was needed. He knew what his role was, and he let me and my posse do our woman thing.

As I have thought about it over the years, I am pretty sure attending a birth is one of the most vulnerable scenarios a man can find himself in. I know, he is not the one squatting totally nude, grunting like a gorilla. Having said that, seeing the mother of his child in this condition is unnerving. Yes, I support the dads, too. **It is their birth experience as well.** I want them to be as involved as they want to be. **Most men desperately want to help and support.** They are like faithful puppies running to you with anticipation and cluelessness panting, "Give me a job, give me a job!"

Retrieving water, adjusting the thermostat, or pushing play on the specified playlist can be about all some men can handle. I'm serious! Even a cold washcloth can be too much. Here comes a lukewarm, soaked rag slapped onto the moaning mother's forehead. *Really?*

How about holding his partner's hand? Easy enough. They have mastered that in their relationship, haven't they?

"Honey, you're rubbing the skin off my thumb."

"Stop the death grip every time I have a contraction."

"OMG! Your hand is so hot and sweaty!"

And during the hardest contraction yet, the male in the room should not dare to adjust his arm even though it is numb and turning blue.

"Are you moving? Why are you moving? Stop moving!"

To be fair, it is not their fault. Laboring women have a few more likes and dislikes than non-laboring women, to put it mildly.

How about the "fear factor" men bring into the room while waiting for Baby?

"Excuse me, ma'am? What does cervical effacement mean?"

"Heart decels? Is the baby okay?"

"Shouldn't she be getting drugs now?"

"Wait, is she really gonna leave me?"

There was this one client attempting a VBAC (Vaginal Birth After Cesarean) who had labored for twenty-four hours, and, for a couple of reasons, it was time to head back to the OR for surgery.

The nurses whisked my client away leaving her husband, Jacob, behind with me and my apprentice. He acted like he was on another planet and looked very concerned. His body language was showing tension, and his eyes roamed the room aimlessly. He had not really said much during the entire birth.

One of the nurses returned with a set of scrubs and told Jacob she would be back soon to take him into the OR so he could be with his wife for the birth of their son. When a woman goes back for a Cesarean, the nurses give the appropriate attire to whomever will be supporting the mama during the surgery. The outfit consists of scrub-like pants and a top, a hat, booties for your shoes, and a mask.

I decided it was time to check in with him and get a gauge on how he was doing. My simple question of, "What's going through your head right now?" led to fifteen minutes of nonstop talking.

The three of us were just sitting there as he admitted he was feeling a little nervous. He then talked about their first child, his job, the doctor's credentials, and back to feeling like he was unprepared. He was clearly processing, and we did want to interrupt.

While Jacob was talking, he stood up and began to unfold the very thin paper scrubs. He then slipped his shoes off and proceeded to undo his pants, next, the zipper... *wait, wait, wait, hold on just a minute; what's happening?*

Jacob was lost in thought and obviously did not realize that these scrubs go OVER your clothes. My apprentice and I quickly glanced at one another. *Now what?* I guess we will focus on his face and words as we receive this striptease.

He pulled his pants down, and all my apprentice could do was look up at the ceiling. He was standing right in front of me, talking away, and I just kept shaking my head "yes" to let him know he had my attention. *Boy, did he have my attention.*

There seemed to be no appropriate gap in his line of thought to interject that he needed to remain clothed at all times. Off went the shirt. *C'est La Vie.*

When the nurse came back to get Jacob, we reassured him that everything was going to be okay. After he left, my apprentice and I immediately grabbed one another, exchanged faces of disbelief, and began to laugh hysterically. *What the hell just happened?* Oh, I know, there was a man in the room who had lost his mind to fear.

That fear and emotion sometimes tend to be unleashed once Baby is born, and more often than not with tears… estrogen-type tears.

"Oh my goodness, I thought she was gonna die!"

"Look at that, it really is a baby."

"I can't believe how strong my wife is."

"Whoa! Thank God I don't have to do that!"

This is totally normal and, quite frankly, adorable.

Never fear though, men, you have a very distinct role that no one else can bring to the table. When my client hears the person she is having a baby with say, "I'm so proud of you," "You're amazing," "You are so beautiful," "Our baby is almost here"; she gets recharged in a special way.

The laboring mom wants to work harder to deliver their baby when she sees her partner in awe of her. The love and admiration her man can give her deliver a powerful emotion and hormone (oxytocin) that allow the mom to feel like she can conquer the world! **No one else in the room will be sharing this baby and all the wonder and surprises that come with it.** They have a future and a life beyond these four walls. What an amazing presence these couples can bring!

Some men can smile, dance, tell jokes, and carry on conversations throughout the whole birth. Others are on their computers, texting loved ones, staying out of the way, and asking me, "How much longer do you think it will be?" No matter what he does or does not do, says, or does not say, almost every woman I know would say she would never want to give birth without her man by her side. Here is a closer look at a few more of my favorite daddy stories.

This story is about a flaming redhead named Brodie. He is the husband of one of my Sobbing Mommies, Evelyn, and when they interviewed me it was clear why I was being hired. He was not into the whole childbirth scene and could not understand why Evelyn wanted to give birth naturally. He knew (and so did she) that he was not up for the task at hand. I assumed that come Game Day, he would let go of all his inhibitions and follow my lead. Boy, was I wrong.

At first, Evelyn was doing a great job of breathing and walking around calmly. I would encourage and help Brodie by having him hold her hand or give her some ice.

Within minutes, very quietly, and without anyone noticing, he had abandoned his post. Brodie was in and out of the room constantly. He would go check on the family in the waiting room, grab a snack, and at times, leave for no apparent reason. More often than not, he would just leave without any word or explanation at all. I am not talking about ten to thirty minutes. I mean MIA for an hour at a time. This was one of my first experiences where the dad truly did not want to be involved.

I continued to try to get him somewhat invested in the process, but he would just respond with, "I'm good. I don't really have a need to jump in like that." *Hmmm. Maybe Evelyn has a need for you to jump in.* He was not as fiery as his hair might suggest.

My thoughts were headed towards judgments of him. I know, I know, wrong on so many levels! I did warn you that this was one of my first experiences of the man in the room clearly not comfortable with birth at all. I should have taken my cues from Evelyn. She never asked him for help, never asked him questions or, now that I think about it, never really even looked at him. She knew exactly how this day would go. Brodie simply was not into or capable of the kind of support she needed during childbirth.

Birth finally took a turn toward becoming very intense, and Evelyn was struggling with every contraction. It was time. Evelyn was on the bed and starting to push. The doctor came into the room, and Brodie made a beeline for the door.

"Brodie." I held up my hand for him to stop.

He did, and Evelyn pushed again.

As he bolted for the door, I whispered, "Brodie, wait. Your baby is about to be here."

He stopped, and I motioned for him to come over with me. He took a couple of steps backward, then hid behind the curtain barely peeking with one eye, like a child hiding from a scary movie that was on TV.

Baby was crowning, and Evelyn was getting louder. Brodie had one hand on the doorknob and was not peeking at all.

Just a few short minutes went by, then, "HUUUUUUUAAAAAAH!"

"WOO-HOO! Baby is here!"

Evelyn cried while holding her baby, and dad was nowhere to be seen.

Now, I rarely walk away from a client right after Baby is born, but in this case, I just had to try to get Brodie to engage. I walked over to the door, which was cracked, and he was right outside the room, white-knuckled, squeezing the doorknob. Y'all, his face was white from fear and green from nausea at the same time!

"He's here, Brodie. It's over. Come see your baby."

His eyes were closed, but I grabbed his hand and led him over to Evelyn's bedside.

"Brodie, honey. Look."

He opened his eyes to find a baby boy with a head full of red hair. Yes! Red hair! He looked like a little man. Brodie burst into tears. *Wow! Was I wrong about Brodie?* He was sobbing, truly; snot and everything. **He was not indifferent, bored, or aloof; he was scared.**

But then, he smiled and looked into his wife's eyes with such affection and admiration. So beautiful! Brodie was fully engaged while the nurses washed his baby's hair and tried to comb it over. Nope, his hair stood straight up. He looked like a mix between his daddy and Conan O'Brien. The nurses took him all around the Labor and Delivery floor and showed him off to everyone.

Fast forward. Brodie is a wonderful dad, and I am the first person that HE calls when they get pregnant. I have been to all of their births, and each time as Evelyn would get braver and stronger, Brodie would be a little bit harder to find.

Some men just roll with the punches and others, like Brodie, dodge them. Nelson *threw* the punches. He was sarcastic, witty, and funny. He was in it for the shock factor. Generally speaking, it took a little time to figure him out.

At my first meeting with Nelson and Faith, the very first thing she told me about him before he arrived was, "Please do not get offended by my husband. He's harmless but says things that might make your jaw drop. I hope he won't keep you from working with us."

Say what?

I do not remember everything he said at that meeting but NOTHING was a straight answer. I believe at one point I asked how he felt about this whole process, natural childbirth, and supporting Faith in what she wanted.

"I have no idea why she wants to do this. It's quite silly. I have no intention of supporting her. She's on her own; unless she wants to hire you." This was all said with a straight face and Faith staring at him.

When the meeting ended, we were saying our goodbyes and, like I always do, I reminded them to think it over and let me know if they would like to move forward in hiring me.

"There's not anything to think about, really. If she wants to spend her own money, that's up to her. I don't much care."

Yikes!

"Micah, please don't listen to him."

"What do you mean, 'don't listen to him?' I think she should take me very seriously."

I was at a loss.

However, over the next several months, I began to understand that Nelson was a very sweet and generous guy. Of course, anytime I would compliment him or tell him thanks, he would quickly deflect and say something like, "I don't know why you're thanking me. I'm planning on leaving for vacay as soon as the baby is born."

Ah… thanks, Seinfeld.

In my first birth experience with them, Faith was laboring like a champ and ready to try the tub. I asked if she brought another bra with her so that she was not stuck with a wet one for the rest of her hospital stay. She said no, so she opted to take that one off to keep it dry.

"Heeeeyyy, look at those!" Nelson said with a huge smile and gawked like a teenage boy with a

Sports Illustrated Swimsuit Edition. He got a few laughs, and that is all it took; he was on.

Faith's water broke, and Nelson offered his wisdom. "Looks like a cow peeing!"

Very nice, Kramer. Cue rolled eyes.

Nelson might be a clown, but he was very involved and supportive. She was leaning on his arm, and I told her just one more push.

"I don't think I can handle one more!" That was Nelson, not Faith... Nelson.

Baby was born, and he looked over at me. "That was exhausting! I need a minute."

... and there's George.

The second birth I attended for them was filmed by one of my doula team members for future coaching purposes. Faith was progressing quickly and so was the intensity. In this video, you could see her transitioning in the tub, on the potty, and enduring vaginal exams designed to move the cervix.

Nelson contributed a few faces, lots of smiles, and thumbs up for the video as if it was a Fourth of July family reunion. He also did a bit of coaching.

"Oooh, come on, you can do it. Just push."

I might have smacked him for that one.

He also reminisced about their time before coming to the hospital.

"Ah, to think how good I was sleeping last night and you waking me up because you couldn't hold it for another few hours."

Smack, punch, dropkick!

At the end of the video, he was "interviewed."

"Hope you enjoyed watching this birth presented by Faith. Now, I did a lot of work. That's not something you should typically expect from your husbands. But... I am perfect. Take care, all, and be sure to watch it again."

Is he hosting The Tonight Show?

I will say, Faith's births are two of my favorites. She is an amazingly strong woman and knows how to birth a baby! She mentioned she wanted to do it again, and that is where I found my rhythm with Nelson to finally throw a punch back at him.

"The next one is a home birth, bro!" I finally caught him off guard.

Now who doesn't know who's serious or not?

In this next story, we have a man who was very serious about his job. This birth was one of the most entertaining ones I had been to. Jordan and Dwayne were a young couple, and they were both physical trainers. They were full of energy; fit and fun. Like most things in their life, natural was the way to go.

Let me tell you, Jordan was a champ! She was physically and mentally prepared to do the hard work, and she had this labor thing down. Dwayne was supportive and all in for whatever Jordan was up for. This dad was not just sitting back in a chair. He was standing, pacing, and focused on his wife. Then transition started.

It was getting real, and Jordan clearly needed more guidance. Dwayne was ready to go. He would repeat the phrases that I used to affirm and rally Jordan towards her goal. While she was finding her strength and rhythm, he was right beside her matching her desire and intensity.

Of course, Dwayne knew how to support and motivate someone when they were doing something hard; especially physically hard. As a fitness trainer, he understood that so much of what people needed was mental resolve and a belief that they could do it! This guy was a natural!

It was time for Jordan to start pushing, and she decided to stand. At one point, she had her foot on a low stool and lunged into the contractions to help open up her hips and allow Baby to descend even further. Jordan started off initially just bearing down, which can be effective if you have a baby that seems to be coming all on its own; no pushing required. A few contractions went by, and I gave Jordan a little more instruction.

"Jordan, when that contraction starts to build, get a really good deep breath. Then you're gonna want to 'trap' all of that power and go towards the pressure you feel. You're no longer exhaling slowly and letting all the air come down and out. It's time to do something with that contraction and push the pain out of your bottom. The nurse is gonna count to ten. Try and apply all your power for the full ten seconds. Then get another good deep breath, and we'll start the count again. We'll do that three times. You ready? Here comes another contraction. Fill those lungs and trap all that power. Don't let it out."

Jordan's nurse began to count. "And one, two, three... great job, five, six, seven... you're almost there, nine, and ten."

I think Dwayne started to feel more and more in his element as Jordan started pushing because it was something he could coach her through. She was also lunging through contractions, so she looked like an athlete who was on rep fifty with only fifty more to go. Dwayne was there right along with me, echoing my instructions and counting. I continued to coach.

"Great Jordan! Get another deep breath, and now, push!"

"Go, Jordan, breathe, one, two, push! Five, six, I mean four, five! Let's do this!"

"A little more, Jordan, all in your bottom."

"Come on, babe! Eight, nine, you gotta give us more than that! Push and TEN!"

His volume became a little louder and the tone stronger. He was fully in personal trainer mode. I noticed that Jordan had that look on her face; a glazed, primal grunt of sheer power. She found it... the Sweet Spot! I was ready to lead her to victory.

"That was it, Jordan. Stay with that. Go towards it."

And so was Dwayne. He looked at me and flashed a smile. He was ALL IN!

"You gotta give more and ONE, PUSH, THREE, PUSH, FIVE, PUSH!!"

Jordan's contraction was over.

"Great job, Jordan. Could you feel that?"

She shook her head yes.

"Perfect. You just keep doing that, and Baby will be here soon."

"That was it, babe! You can do this! You were made for this! Now dig deep and FINISH!" Great words of truth and so much passion came from Dwayne.

One of the nurses in the room gave instruction. "Okay, here comes another one, fill those lungs and one, two, three…"

"Let's go! FIVE, SIX, COME ON GIRL… SEVEN, EIGHT, YOU'RE NOT DONE, NINE, TEN! WOOHOO! That's my girl!"

I was in utter shock. The nurses and I stared at one other. He was so loud and so intense! Another contraction came, and Dwayne was not waiting on anybody.

"Time to dig DEEP! Show me more! Let's GOOOOO!"

There was that look again in Jordan's eyes: determination and a little fear.

"There you go, Jordan. That's the one. Stick with that right there."

"YES MA'AM! ALL YOU! It's ALL YOU! FOUR, FIVE... YOU'RE NOT DONE YET! FINISH STRONG! THAT'S MY GIRL!"

He was yelling and clapping loudly. In his mind, he was back in his gym with his buddies, willing them on to victory.

"ALRIGHT, ALRIGHT!" Dwayne moved toward Jordan and got right in her face, tensed his body, and focused his eyes. "YOU CAN DO THIS, JORDAN! GIVE IT ALL YOU'VE GOT!"

He was truly motivating, but there was genuine concern that the entire Labor and Delivery wing had heard every word. Jordan was not shaken in the least. She thrived on her husband's approach.

Another contraction came, and Jordan started to grunt, which turned into a yell.

Dwayne stayed right in her face. "Don't you quit on me now, girl! DON'T YOU QUIT ON ME NOW, GIRL!"

"AAAAHHHHH! OOOOUUUCH!"

"THAT'S RIGHT! IT'S RIGHT HERE, IT'S RIGHT NOW, GOTTA DIG DEEPER!"

It was like there was no one else in the room except Dwayne and Jordan. Check that; no one else in the hospital except Dwayne and Jordan.

I felt a little bad breaking up this moment. "Okay, Jordan, baby's head is crowning. Give me a big push."

"THIS IS IT, BABE! PUSH, PUSH, PUSH, PUSH! I CAN SEE HER HEAD! JORDAN, I CAN SEE HER HEAD! GO, GO, GO! DON'T STOP!"

The doctor interjected. "Stop, Jordan, don't push. Let Baby stretch your perineum."

"OOOOOOWWWEEEE!!!"

"YOU'RE OKAY! THIS IS NOTHIN'! YOU GOT THIS!"

Let me elaborate for you, Coach.

"Jordan, take a deep breath and blow it out long and slow. Let your bottom sink into the bed. That's Baby that you're feeling, and you are almost done. One more big push and you'll be holding you're little one."

"I can't do it. It hurts so bad. AAAAAAHHHHH! AAAAAAAHHHH!"

"THIS IS NOTHIN! YOU'RE STRONGER THAN THAT!"

"OOOOOOHHHHHHH! WAAAAT IS THAAAAAT!?"

"Jordan, that's Baby's head. You've gotta really bear down and give us one big push."

"DID YOU HERE THAT? LET'S GO! LET ME SEE WHATCHYA GOT! DO IT DO IT!"

"AAAAAHHHH! UUUUUUUHHHHH!"

"There you go, Jordan. That's it. She's here!"

"OH MY GOSH, BABE! WE DID IT! WE DID IT! SHE'S HERE! YEEAAHHH!"

Normally, I would have judged a man that said, "we did it," but in this case, I knew exactly what he meant, so I let it slide.

"That's my girl! I KNEW YOU COULD DO IT! I'm so proud of you, babe!"

Jordan looked up at me and smiled. "I couldn't have done it without you, Micah!"

What the what?! I was not expecting that!

Dwayne walked over to me, and I received a huge embrace complete with being lifted off the floor from this tearful new dad.

"Oh my goodness, Micah, I wouldn't have known what to do if it wasn't for you! I was so scared, and I wasn't sure how this was all gonna go."

For real? Could have fooled me, Coach!

Having these men by their woman's side is a treat! **They are all different and add their own flavor to the birth room.** We would not want it any other way.

CHAPTER 14

all in the family

*W*HAT ABOUT OTHER PEOPLE a woman might invite to attend her birth? For so many women, birth is a private affair. Occasionally though, you will have a woman who desires friends or family to be near her. I will raise my hand on this. I had a house full of people at my births. Besides my husband, there was ...

First birth:

the midwife

my mom

my mother-in-law

my two sisters

my husband's two sisters

three midwife assistants

... and a partridge in a pear tree.

Second birth:
>   the midwife
>
>   my two sisters
>
>   two friends
>
>   my mom
>
>   my dad
>
>   my stepdad
>
>   my stepmom
>
>   ... let's be honest, that was a little strange.

Third birth:
>   the midwife
>
>   my two sisters
>
>   an apprentice
>
>   ... a small house.

Fourth birth:
>   the midwife
>
>   one sister
>
>   one friend
>
>   two midwife assistants
>
>   my daughter
>
>   ... the same small house, but did not care.

Fifth birth:

> the midwife
>
> my two sisters
>
> three friends
>
> a midwife assistant
>
> my dad
>
> ... and we will go ahead and count the twelve-pound baby I delivered as another whole person in the room.

Sixth birth:

> ... remember, this was the emergency C-section at twenty-seven weeks, so there was no one, including my husband, at the actual birth.

I do not know exactly why, but there was just something very comforting to me about having these supportive people in my corner and, quite literally, in the corner. I have a large family, and I am used to lots of "peeps" in my business. I am also an extrovert (maybe that's it).

Confession, I am addicted to affirmation and praise. I love to hear the "atta girls" and people going on and on about something I am doing well; I thrive on it. **To be honest, that may have been another huge motivation for me in becoming a doula. I felt supported by and relied on these loved ones to help carry me through.** Their encouragement was monumental in my success. If I think about it, I had about eight unofficial doulas at my births. My daddy used to say, "If a little is good, a lot is REAL good." I took that one as one of God's Golden Rules.

It is a great honor to be at someone's birth. At the ones I have attended over the years, I have had some GREAT experiences with my clients and the loved ones who were invited to be with them. I have also had many amusing situations with these beloved friends and family members. When we are talking about family, most of the time it means my client's mom or her sister. On occasion, though rare, it means the whole family! But hey, the more the merrier. *Y'all come on in and enjoy the show.*

One of the first clients of mine who chose to have her whole family there was Tori. At first, it was just her husband, Timmy, then her mama joined them. After about an hour of her mom being on the phone, texting, and calling people, one of Tori's sisters, Glory, showed up. Glory was a talker. She proceeded to inform Tori that her husband, Glen, was on her last nerve. She was frustrated at him because he was complaining about having to watch the kids. A few minutes later, in walked her other sister, Stormi, with her husband Blue. Stormi also had Tori's daughter, Cori, who was quite the handful. She was dancing and singing, telling jokes; she was everywhere.

I noticed that Tori was starting to show signs of more intense contractions; however, the action in the room did not stop. In fact, to Glory's surprise, Glen strolled in with their two children, Lori, and Chloe. Y'all keepin' up?

"What the hell are you doin' here?" A very heated discussion broke out between Glory and Glen. I wondered if anyone else had noticed that Tori was really having to focus on her breathing. Her eyes were closed while she rolled her hips around on the birthing ball.

I decided to check on her once her contraction was over. "Hey, girl? How ya holdin' up?"

"I'm good. They're getting more intense, and I'm ready to go."

"You're doing so good. Just let me know if you need the room to be a little quieter so you can focus as your contractions get more intense."

"Who? Them? They're not gonna get quieter. They're fine."

Alrighty, girl. You do you.

The conversation turned to food because no one had eaten lunch yet. Of course, Glen decided to stay, and Tori's mom piped up to take control.

"Now, y'all listen up. Somebody is gonna have to call this in, and somebody has got to go pick it up." She was a brilliant woman.

"Mama, hush. Glen, you take Cori, Lori, and Chloe with you to pick up some pizza at the Hut. Stormi and I will call it in. Blue, do you want to go with Glen and the kids?"

All these names, I'm lost. Who's going where? Apparently, Glory was the matriarch in the family because nobody interjected and everyone said, "Yes, ma'am."

My client's husband, Timmy, finally emerged

from the corner. "I'm not sure Tori is gonna be up for a pizza party."

"Timmy, I am perfectly fine, and I know everybody is hungry. Hell, I'm gonna be hungry once this baby is born. Now y'all hurry on back and be safe."

Yes, please. Y'all hurry on back with Canadian bacon and pineapple for me and pick up Rori, Stori, and Dori on the way.

That's right, we had a pizza party right up until it was time to push. It was like Grand Central Station during lunch hour in the waiting room.

I had another sweet client that was very close to her extended family. Barb was having her second baby. Her oldest was twenty-two years old, so, needless to say, this baby was a joyful surprise. Barb was about forty-five-years-old and was dealing with a couple of health issues. One in particular that was affecting her pregnancy was high blood pressure.

For geriatric pregnancies, most doctors want to induce birth as soon as practical, and her doctor was no exception. My client was unfazed by this and was firm that she was going to wait.

Fast forward to when she was forty-two weeks pregnant, and it was time to get things moving whether she wanted to or not. Barb was supposed to go in the night before her induction, but she told her doctor that she would see him around eight the next morning. Barb don't play, y'all. I arrived around ten o'clock that morning because not much was happening before that, or so I thought.

"Micah, come in! I'm so happy to see you! I want you to meet my family."

It's a full house, yo.

"Hey, Barb! You look great! I'd love to meet the fam."

"Okay. This is my mama, Georgia, and my Auntie Flo. Karen is Auntie Flo's daughter and beside her is my second cousin, Ruby. Now over here is my Nana, and behind her in the rocking chair is my great grandmamma, Honey. Of course, you and Nick have already met."

Wow! What a fabulous heritage! I loved that she was being supported by all these amazing women who have gone before her.

"Hello, everyone. So thankful to meet you all. And how are you holdin' up, Nick, surrounded by all these beautiful women?"

A symphony of voices rang out.

"Oh, look at you. How sweet you are!"

"Well, my goodness! Such a beautiful young woman."

"We are so blessed to have you here. Thank you for taking care of my girl Barb. Now, we've all been talkin', and we are concerned that Barb is not listening to the doctor."

"Now, child, we've known Dr. Shepherd since he was an intern. In fact, he delivered Barb!"

Exactly how old is Dr. Shepherd? I had never worked with him before that day, but he had a reputation. This man was old school, and I do not mean "house-calls-for-home-births" old school. I mean "stay-in-the-bed, IV, drugs, episiotomies, vacuum, spanking Baby's bottom" old school.

"He is a wonderful doctor, and we trust him completely!"

Nana turned around to Honey and spoke in a very loud, slow voice. "MAMA! MAMA? DID YOU HEAR WHAT I SAID ABOUT DR. SHEPHERD?

TELL BARB AND HER FRIEND HOW
WONDERFUL HE IS."

Y'all, the sweetest little old woman slowly got
out of the rocking chair. She shuffled over to Barb's
bedside.

"Somebody is callin' me, and I'm sure it's
important. Let me tell you... Uh, Georgia, take me
to the bathroom."

I laughed out loud. This whole scene was high
entertainment. However, I was not sure those
sweet women were there to support Barb and her
decisions. It appeared they were there to make sure
she did what THEY thought was best. Now, the last
thing you want is for a posse of "sweet" old
Southern women to start telling you how it is.

Auntie Flo spoke up. "Micah, let's you and me
go find the doctor and let him know we are ready
to follow his lead."

"And tell him that Barb has changed her mind
and wants to go ahead and have her water broken,"
another voice resounded.

WHOA! Hold the boat! I was getting roped in.
Thank goodness for good ol' "Saint" Nick.

"Alright, alright, that's enough, you schemin' little hussies. You all need to behave, or you're gonna be sayin' your good-byes."

Laughter erupted, and they were all smiles and innocent faces.

"Oh now, we didn't mean any harm, sweetie."

"We're as innocent as Sunday school girls."

Laughter and agreement of their pure intentions persisted. I was enjoying this ever so much.

Barb started to speak. "Mama, Nana, Auntie, I know you all mean well, and I want you to stay. However, this is gonna be done my way. Dr. Shepherd knows where I stand, and he also knows he has a fan club in here."

On cue like a gospel choir, they sang out.

"Well now ain't that the truth."

"He absolutely does."

"I would trust him with my life."

"Is someone gonna take me to the bathroom? I'm gonna wet myself."

"Oh, Honey, I'm sorry. Yes, ma'am, I'll take you now."

Anyone else want to voluntarily leave to help Honey to the restroom?

Nick spoke up again. "How about you all go grab some coffee? It's still gonna be awhile before this little guy graces us with his presence. We will call straight away if things start changing quickly."

Everyone agreed this was a great idea, and they started the processional out the door.

"Now, Micah, we are not far, and you give us a holler if you need anything at all."

"Yes, ma'am. I certainly will."

While I was grateful to have the opportunity to have a heart-to-heart with Barb, I was also looking forward to this amazing "village" coming back to join us. Barb and I discussed our game plan, and so much of it had to do with her not trusting her doctor. She was absolutely game for getting things going, but she did not want him to touch her. *Houston, we have a problem.* Fortunately, I knew Barb's nurse well, and I caught her up on our situation. Let's just say that during a routine exam, Barb's water "suddenly" broke. *Problem solved.* Things picked up immediately, and Barb's family returned.

"Now see, Barb, we told you that Dr. Shepherd knows what he's talking about."

"When will he be joining us?"

"Yes, we can't wait to see him."

I addressed the crowd. "Ladies, it won't be long now because Barb will be pushing soon."

"Oh, thank goodness you're here, Micah."

I kept my word. Barb began pushing about thirty minutes later.

Enter Dr. Shepherd. "Well, hello, everyone."

"Oh my goodness, Dr. Shepherd!"

"Well, bless my heart! It's so good to see you!"

"Thank goodness you're here now!"

"We've been anticipating your return!"

Were they expecting Jesus and the rapture?

"Well, thank you, ladies. So good to see you all again. So Barb, you ready to have this baby?"

"Yes, sir. I am."

Barb began to push, and, in the "not so far" distance, a myriad of coaches began to chatter.

'"Yes, sweet girl. Give it all you got."

"Push, my baby. You gotta push, push!"

"Come on now. We want to see that baby."

"Barb, don't you want some pain meds?"

Once the contraction was over, "Dr. McDreamy" spoke to his followers. "Ladies, you are doing an excellent job. How 'bout we save the cheers and instructions for the nurses and me."

Georgia spoke up. "Of course, Doctor, and don't forget Micah. She is the 'abba-daba-adoooula.'"

Hadn't been called that before!

Nana concurred. "She is wonderful."

The nurse chimed in with the information Dr. Shepherd had been chomping at the bit to hear. He had been very anxious for his "at risk" patient to have this baby weeks ago.

"Dr. Shepherd, this is Micah Burgess, and she is an essential part of the team. Upon her arrival, everything has picked up with Barb. Her coaching has been instrumental in the progress you see right now."

I introduced myself. "Nice to meet you, Dr. Shepherd. I promise I will not be in your way, and I'm here to help keep Barb focused and calm. Let me know if there is anything else I can help with."

"Terrific! I genuinely appreciate all that you have done."

"Make no mistake sir, Barb has done all the work. And you're ready to have this baby, right Barb?"

"Let's do this!"

Another contraction started, and Barb began to push. To their credit, Barb's family stayed quiet, but the room was not void of all their positive energy. You could feel the "Hallelujah Chorus" almost bursting through the seams of their shut mouths. They did not have to wait long.

Two contractions later, the head was born but a shoulder was stuck. There was no time for panic. Dr. Shepherd stood up from his stool, put one knee on the edge of the bed, reached inside for the shoulder, turned that baby, and Barb pushed him out. The old school doctor had done that before. Impressive! So thankful he was there because not every doctor has that kind of skill under pressure.

Nick informed the Great Cloud of Witnesses. "He's here, ladies!"

Dr. Shepherd turned around to give his admirers a quick peek of Baby before laying him on mama's chest.

"OHH MYYY! Thank you so much, Dr. Shepherd!"

"Look at that sweet boy!"

"What an excellent job you did, sir!"

"Yes, thank you, Dr. Shepherd! WE couldn't have done it without you!"

Awwwww, let the old "hussies" have their fun.

Finally, one of the funniest family encounters I had was at Dolorian's birth. She and her husband, Anthony, invited ten family members to be with them during the birth of their firstborn son. This was not including the midwife, two nurses, a photographer, and me.

Well, we had ourselves quite a crowd, not unlike a typical turnout of spectators for a select soccer match. It was complete with popcorn, candy, nachos, and coke (that's Texan for soda or pop). There was the constant sound of chatting, laughing, eating, and even cheering. It felt like the World Cup Soccer Tournament was on... GOOOOOOOOOOAL!!!

Labor was going just fine and, believe it or not, it was quite pleasant in the room. It felt so natural.

As Dolorian got closer to transition, she obviously had to focus quite a bit more. I could hear her starting to bear down a little. Right on cue, the midwife came in to check her progress and was shocked to find sixteen people in the room; six of whom were standing right in front of the doorway.

"Ummmm. Hello?"

Everyone stopped and turned to look at her. She looked around quite puzzled, and, after a couple of seconds, continued.

"I'm sorry, but there are just too many people in here. How did you all get in here?"

She stared at one of the nurses, then Dolorian jumped in.

"I want them all here. Is this gonna be a problem?"

I knew exactly what the midwife was going to say because it was actually true.

"Well, first of all, I can't even get to you."

In an instant, ten people moved and gathered to the far side of the room. It was like the parting of the Red Sea. *There you go, come on in.* Dolorian and the midwife continued their conversation.

"Thank you. There's really not gonna be enough room for all of these people, the delivery table, and the extra nurses."

"I understand, but this is what I really want for my birth experience."

"Dolorian, there are hospital policies about how many people can be in the room at a time. Now, how do you want to do this because I'm here to do a vaginal exam?"

"Actually, I need to go to the restroom first. Can you come back in about ten minutes?"

"Sure thing. That will give your family a chance to say goodbye and head on out."

"Okay, thank you SOOO much."

Everyone in the room caught Dolorian's full meaning with that statement. The midwife left, and Dolorian sprang into action.

She looked at the nurse. "If you don't want to be a party to what's about to happen, then you might want to leave."

The nurse excused herself. She wanted to be able to claim no prior knowledge. Smart cookie.

"Okay, everyone behind that curtain."

There was a curtain in the corner of the room that obscured a very large tub. That's right... ten people climbed into the tub. There was so much talking and laughing.

"SHHHHH. You guys have to be quiet!"

They quieted down but continued whispering until the midwife and nurse reentered the room. Total silence.

"Okay, Dolorian. That's much better, don't you think?"

Dolorian did not answer because she was already pushing.

"Let's have a look and see what's going on."

The midwife put on her gloves and announced, "Gracious! The head is already crowning! Somebody get me my cover-up."

Ain't gonna be any time for that, lady.

Dolorian let out a giant grunt that turned into a yell.

I jumped in with some affirmation. "The head's here, girl! You've got this! One more big push."

"UUUUUUUUAAAAAAAAAAAAAH!"

Anthony proclaimed loudly, "MY BOY! HE'S HERE!"

GOOOOOOOOOOAL!!

You guessed it. An eruption of robust cheers came from the bathtub.

"WOOOH HOOOHH!"

"ALRIGHT!"

"SHE DID IT!"

"YAAAAAAAY!"

"HAAAAAAAAY!"

"HE'S HERE!"

The midwife jumped and almost dropped that baby. It was like those old jack-in-the-box toys. You crank it and crank it while this little tune plays, then... POP! Instant cardiac arrest! The mob jerked back the curtain and, with whistles and cheers, charged the bed. I stood next to Dolorian not knowing if I should protect her from the stampede, go check on the midwife, or simply just laugh out loud at what was happening.

"OOOH MY GOODNESS! LOOK AT HIM!"

"YOU OKAY, MAMA?"

Dolorian responded with a huge smile, Baby in arms, "I'm great because he's here, and you're all here, too!"

I am a sucker for happy endings and women getting what they want. **You want to host a party or a family reunion... you do you, girl.**

CHAPTER 15

yo, mama

*L*ET'S NARROW THE FIELD down a little. Are you considering having your mama at your birth? Let me talk about mine first. Her name is Millie. We lived in the same town for my first two births, which are the ones she has attended. She is gentle, supportive, and strong enough to take on just about anything. She brings a quiet inner strength, and, to this day, I lean on her. This is the side of her that most people will encounter. However, she does have a witty, feisty spirit about her. She is funny with a hint of sarcasm. I learned from the best.

My first birth was pretty fast and quite the whirlwind. There was not much to do. She was in the background but continually watching me with awe and smiles. It was not until after the baby was born, and I was recovering from a hematoma and mastitis, that she piped up. My midwife was giving some instructions about my care, and Millie sprang into action.

"So, Micah is gonna need some bed rest for a couple of weeks. There are several things to do for her care. She'll need a sitz bath with Red Raspberry Leaf tea, comfrey, plantain, lavender, and yarrow flowers. For her fever, Vitamin C, lots of water, and garlic. For topical relief for her breasts, get some cabbage leaves, shredded potatoes, and sea salt."

"I'm sorry. What are we doin' here, makin' soup? My daughter is sick, not hungry!"

"We're gonna go with a more natural approach."

"Okay. So, you want me to go grocery shoppin' and NOT to the pharmacy?"

My midwife giggled, then left the room.

"Micah, you just tell me when you're done with all the Kumbaya stuff, and I'll go get you something that will knock you out cold."

Classic Millie!

At my second birth we were playing cards together, and the atmosphere was so relaxed and way slower than the first. I took a walk, ate lunch, took a bath, rested, it was great! For some reason, my mama was becoming concerned, so she had a heart-to-heart with my midwife, Connie.

"Excuse me, Connie? Do you have a minute? I'm just wanting to get your thoughts on what's happening. Doesn't look like Micah wants to have a baby today. I think it's high time she gets focused. Don't you?"

"Actually, I think it's going quite well. This is Micah's birth, and we will follow her lead. I'm pretty sure she's progressing just fine."

"*Well, bless your heart.* That wasn't helpful at all. Thanks, anyway."

She cracks me up; she is truly the funniest person I know.

Now, what you need to know is that most women DO NOT want their mothers at their birth. There are a few reasons for this. **They do not want their mothers to worry or stress them out, and they do not want to be mothered.** That's fair.

So, it is rare when one of my clients invites her mom. Typically, this mom has been given very strict instructions: Do not interfere or ask a lot of questions, do not get in the way, and do not tell me what to do. Mostly, a mother is a spectator.

There are some mamas who do not respond well to their daughter denying them "the right" to be there for the birth of their grandchild. We actually had one mother attempt several times to sneak into her daughter's room. Did she not think her daughter knew that she would be pulling out all the stops to get back there? She had already prepared the staff for this.

"Labor and Delivery, how can I help you?"

"Yes, I'm here for Janet Breadstone, Room 212."

"I'm sorry, ma'am, that room is not accepting any visitors at this time."

"Oh. I'm not a visitor. I'm her mother. Can you please call her room and let her know that I'm here?"

"Yes, ma'am, I will call that room, but they've already instructed us that no one is to come back. Give me just a second."

Now keep in mind that Janet's mom, Helen, had been calling and texting for about an hour.

They had already told her there was no need to come to the hospital because they were not wanting anyone back there with them.

I think the reply text went something like, "Well that's not true. You're letting that *adooooola* back there with you. It should be me!"

My client finally stopped responding to her and turned off her phone to no avail.

"Ma'am, room 212 is not receiving any visitors at this time."

"Well, that little b****. Listen, that's my grandbaby back there. Don't I have some kind of rights?!"

Yes. You have the right to remain silent.

"I'm sorry, ma'am. This patient is under our care, and we respect her wishes. You'll need to wait in the waiting area."

"Oh, you people. Fine!"

After this exchange, the nurse let us know what had happened.

"I knew it! I just knew it. Trust me, she's gonna figure out a way to get back here."

"Well, if she does, Janet, I'm happy to be the bad guy. I have no problem being a bouncer."

About thirty minutes went by, and the front desk buzzed the room.

"Mrs. Breadstone? Did someone from your room order a pizza to be delivered? I said they could leave it at the front desk, but they are insistent that you want it delivered to your room."

She's creative. I'll give her that.

"Absolutely not! We didn't order a pizza. That's Mom just trying a different angle."

"Okay. Thank you, and we'll take care of it."

Make sure that pizza stays with us. Yes, doulas get hungry.

"That woman! I swear, how did I survive all these years? Well, I'm stressed now! Thanks a lot, Mom!"

"Janet, I don't want you to give this another thought. I'll go talk to the staff and take care of this once and for all. All you need to do is relax. In fact, let me go ahead and get a bath drawn for you."

"Oh, perfect! Thank you, Micah."

I started the bath and left the room. I found our nurse, the charge nurse, and the front desk clerk on the Labor and Delivery floor.

"Okay, listen, you guys. Let's not even call back to Janet's room anymore. There is no one they are expecting right now. If there is a question or something you guys can't ignore, and it needs to be addressed, then just text me instead, and we'll communicate that way. Sound good?"

"Yep. Sounds great! So sorry this is happening, and we'll be more vigilant."

"It's not y'alls fault. Thanks so much for going the extra mile."

I headed back to the room to get Janet settled into the bath. She was definitely relaxing now. Her labor was progressing well, and contractions were getting stronger. After about an hour in the bath, twenty minutes of walking, and three contractions on the potty, Janet started to talk about pressure. We headed to the bed for an exam. Janet was complete, and it was time to start pushing.

"This is it, my friend! You've endured the hard part. Now you get to do something about what you're feeling. You ready to meet this baby?"

"Absolutely! I can't believe she's about to be here!"

For the first three, I coached her on how to produce effective contractions. We talked about relaxing her bottom, focusing her pushes, and using her strength down low. She was getting the hang of it pretty quickly. She started another contraction and took a deep breath.

"HUUUUUUUU... AAAH... WHAT'S THAT NOISE!?"

There was some sort of commotion out in the hall. We could hear several voices getting louder while my client was trying to push.

"AAARE YOOOU KIDDING MEEE?!"

Then it was clear.

"Ma'am, please! You can't go in there!"

"That's my baby in there! You can't keep me from her!"

"Are you FOR REAL?! MOMMMM! Y'all... AAAAAAAAAAAAAAAH!"

We then heard a couple of male voices.

"Let's go, ma'am. You've already been warned, and you're refusing to cooperate. We are escorting you out of the building."

SECURITY! SE-KER-I-TY! You got to go. You have got to go!

"Thank God! My mama; she's so stubborn!"

Ummmm. I think it's a little worse than that. I think you've got yourself a Glen Close, "Fatal Attraction" type situation goin' on here. Cray-cray!

We found out later that Janet's mom got in by waiting in the hallway until a large group of people walked through the doors of the Labor and Delivery floor. The front desk clerk immediately spotted her and called security. She commanded Helen to stop. Helen kept walking but walked aimlessly because she was not sure where room 212 was. She eventually found it, but another nurse was following her as well. Unfortunately for Helen, Janet had her all figured out. She had been intentionally given the wrong room number. Janet was actually two doors down from room 212, which was empty. This deception kept her semi-contained until security arrived. I guess I did not have to worry about Janet. She had this birth on lockdown.

Not all mamas are crazy when it comes to their daughters. As a mom myself, I can say that we are slightly obsessed, overbearing, smothering, and passionate, where our daughters are concerned. That's all. We want what is best for them, and we still think we have the corner market on that, even when they become adults and are mamas themselves.

I can remember this one sweet couple, Marina and José Santos. They hired me for the birth of their second child. Her first birth was filled with every intervention you can imagine, and she was not happy with the experience. During our interview she asked my opinion on having her mother there. I asked her some questions about her relationship with her mom and if she felt supported and comforted by her. She let me know that her mom was very important to her and that they did everything together. That did not exactly answer my question. *Let's take another run at this.*

"That's great to hear how important she is in your life! I guess I'm trying to help you determine if your mom is a peaceful source of strength for you."

"My mother is a very proud, talkative woman."

I'm still not quite getting through.

"When you think about her being in the birthing room, how does that make you feel? Is that a comforting thought? Does it make you smile? Are you immediately stressed or worried?"

"No, not really."

No to all of it? Why is this so hard?

It finally dawned on me. "Marina, when you think about her NOT being at this birth, how does that make you feel?"

Marina closed her eyes, bowed her head, then proceeded to do the sign of the cross.

That answers my question. She could not imagine her NOT being there because her mom would not let her imagine her not being there.

"My mother needs to be there."

"Sounds good. This is your choice and your choice alone to make. I support you one hundred percent!"

A few weeks later, we were at the hospital and active labor was in full swing. Marina had labored at home for about five hours, then came to the hospital at six centimeters dilated. That's the way you do it!

We had been at the hospital for about an hour, and we heard a voice in the hallway. There was a rhythmic sound to the words. The door opened and it was Marina's mother, Juanita.

"I said mija que yo iba a coming PRONTO, por qué did you come sola?"

Oh, hello.

It sounded like she was talking about Marina (mija) coming quickly or soon (pronto) but why (por qué) did you come alone (sola)?

"¿Cuánto tiempo piensas que llevará esto? Tuve un día bien largo y quería que tú vinieras por mi casa para que pudiera acompañarte al hospital."

Ah-ha! I heard my house and the hospital.

I was waiting for someone to translate or even give an introduction.

"No estoy contenta que no viniste a buscarme en camino al hospital. Estoy preocupada que no voy a poder terminar la cena antes de que llegue mi esposo. ¿Cuánto tiempo piensas que llevara acabo esto?"

I got nothin'.

It kind of sounded like Juanita was scolding Marina. An opportunity came up for me to discreetly ask José what she was saying. This was his response.

"She basically had a long day. She wanted Marina to come and pick her up and bring her to the hospital, so now she's telling her how unhappy she is that Marina didn't. She's also worried about getting supper done before Marina's dad gets home. She has also asked several times how long she thinks it's going to be."

"Oh. Okay? Does she need anything, or can I help in any way? How do you think Marina is doing with this conversation?"

HA! Conversation? Hardly. This is a one woman show.

"Tu hermano hubiera venido a buscarme para traerme al hospital, pero está bien, mija, porque este es tu día especial yo estoy aquí para ayudarte. ¿Necesitas algo? ¿Tienes hambre? ¿Sabes cuanto tiempo piensas que llevara acabo esto? Porque tu padre va a llegar pronto."

I think I heard "brother, hospital, daughter, why, special, hungry, father, soon." Are we talking about a family dinner at the hospital?

"MAMA! No más!"

Now that, I caught.

This mama continued to speak to her daughter in Spanish the entire labor. She never spoke to José, me, the nurses, or the midwife. She was not loud or mean, she was just constant. I was sure she could hold her breath underwater for five minutes and never come up for air. This was the scene for about an hour, then sweet Marina let out a yelp!

"AAAAAAAAH! WHAT'S HAPPENING?!"

"Tell me what you're feeling, Marina."

"Yo te puedo decir lo que está pasando, mija. ¡Este bebe ya viene! Preparate, mija! Me acuerdo de cuando tu naciste mija…"

"HUUAAH! I can feel something! AAAAHHH!"

I lifted the sheet just a little bit and, lo and behold, there was a head!

"Your baby is here, Marina! Reach down and get him."

"OOOOOOOOOOO, MIJO!"

Juanita rushed to the bed, and I buzzed for the midwife. Marina reached down and looked at her baby coming. With her hands at his head, she gave one more big push.

"Ay, ay, ay, MIJA! ¡LO HICISTE, MIJA! ¡LO HICISTE!"

The rest of the body came shooting out. Marina grabbed her boy and put him on her chest. Juanita began to sob. She opened up her arms and laid her body across Marina and the baby and kept saying the same thing over and over. "Oh, mi corazón! Oh, mi corazón!" *That's why she's here!* Now everyone was crying. Marina wrapped her arms around su mamá and su bebé and smiled contently. **You cannot replace una mamá amorosa (a loving mama).**

Remember how I said that most women do not want their mothers hovering over them during childbirth? Well, Ricky believed that his wife, Karen, actually did want her mother there. Where he got this notion, I have no clue. Especially since Karen said emphatically that she DID NOT WANT HER MOM THERE. She seemed clear and precise, but I am pretty sure there was a little guilt tripping from Ricky going on. I sensed this was an issue throughout pregnancy. I guess we would find out on Game Day.

Karen called me late one night and said that she was having contractions all day long. She was ready to get checked and see what was happening. She said she would text once she knew something and, about an hour later, replied that she was about five centimeters dilated, which is FABULOUS for a first-time mama. I arrived at the hospital and walked into Karen's room.

"Hey girl! Sounds like you're doing great! So proud of you!"

"Thanks, Micah. I'm hangin' in there. Oh, this is my mom, Cindy."

Looks like guilt won.

Cindy was sitting in a chair in the farthest corner of the room. It would take her ten to fifteen steps to get to the bed. *I wonder if this actually counts as her mom being at the birth.*

"So nice to meet you, Cindy. Are you getting excited about meeting your granddaughter?"

"Oh yes. So excited and I'm really happy…"

"SHH. Mom, remember what I said."

Woo-dang! Seen and not heard. Or rather, I better not see you either. I engaged Ricky in a quick conversation.

"Hey Ricky, how's she doin'?"

"I think Karen is doing great!"

"Perfect! How 'bout we walk the halls a little bit."

"That's a good idea. Karen, want your mom to do that with you? I can go grab your pillow back at the house?"

"No, I'm good. Micah and I can just walk, and mom you stay in here and get some rest. It's gonna be a long night."

Sounds like a plan.

So, Ricky left, and Karen and I started walking.

"Oh my gosh, Micah! I can't believe my mom is here."

"What do you mean? You didn't invite her to come?"

"Ricky called her to let her know we were headed to the hospital. That was it. When we arrived, she was already in the waiting room. She started to follow us, and I told her to wait. I went to triage, and they checked me. They got me into a room, then Ricky left to go park the car. When he came back, she was with him. I said, 'What the hell, Ricky?' He said he couldn't just leave her out there all night long. He believes I owe it to her."

"Got it. Well, what do you want to do?"

"I'm just gonna leave it alone. I already warned her not to talk or try to help me!"

"Alrighty. Now that we've covered that, let it go and start telling me how you're feeling otherwise. Let's have a baby, girl!"

"Sounds good."

We talked between contractions and walked for probably an hour. Karen started to get tired and wanted to rest for a little while. When we got back to the room, Cindy was sitting in the rocking chair that was right beside the bed.

"Mother! WHAT ARE YOU DOING?"

Yikes. I am not sure about this, AT ALL!

Ricky responded. "Karen, I put her in a more comfortable chair. She's fine."

Karen gave him a heavy sigh of frustration and the death glare. *This is gonna be fun!*

We got Karen into the bed and rested for about thirty minutes. Soon the contractions were super close together and laying down was very uncomfortable. I suggested having her position to her hands and knees, so we took a few minutes and got her situated. Karen was facing the bed and the back wall, Ricky was standing beside her, and I was standing behind her. Cindy was sitting behind her out of view and behaving better than I had ever seen any mother behave.

Karen began to breathe loudly, then moan deeply during her contractions.

"That is perfect, Karen! Keep doing that right there. So good!"

"Great job, honey."

"Mom! No!"

Cindy quietly whispered, "sorry" under her breath. I shot her a smile and gave her a wink. She smiled back and began to realize that she was not really the issue… it was the woman in pain. We get it, don't we ladies.

"Hey y'all, I think I want to sit now. My knees are starting to hurt."

We got Karen turned around, and I adjusted the bed so that it was like sitting in a chair. Her eyes closed, and she was very relaxed, breathing perfectly. A contraction started.

"Good, deep breath Karen, then blow it out long and slow. Focus just on breathing all of that pressure down and out."

Karen executed perfectly. She did this for a few more contractions.

"Girl! You are managing those contractions beautifully! Your body is making so much change."

"I can definitely feel more pressure in my bottom."

That's what I'm lookin' for.

Karen took another deep breath, and with this one, the moan turned into an achy yell.

"There you go, Karen. Let everything come down. Great job!"

Cindy quietly agreed with a "Mmm hmm!"

"Mom! Seriously?"

She took another deep breath and blew it out. Cindy looked at me and mouthed, "She's doing so good," and gave me a thumbs up.

"Mom, I can see you."

You better stop while you're ahead, sista.

Karen grabbed another deep breath and was ready for her next contraction.

"Perfect, Karen. Now drop those shoulders."

Karen dropped her shoulders and let all the air out. Apparently, Cindy was also holding her breath because she let out a big sigh as well.

"Damn it, mom. I CAN HEAR YOU!"

Karen took another deep breath and mentioned feeling more pressure. Her contraction was starting to come down.

"That's it, Karen. Let that one go away and now all you need to do is rest."

Karen relaxed and honestly looked like she was about to fall asleep. It was very quiet in the room, and all eyes were on Karen. She started to moan and shifted out of her sitting position. She turned back around on her hands and knees and began pushing.

"WOOOOOOOOOOOOOH! OOOOOOOOOH WOW! THAT'S INTENSE!"

"You've got this. Keep doing what you're doing. We're gonna call the nurse and find out if it's time to have this baby."

Cindy looked at me with wide eyes and ever so slightly gasped.

"MOM! STOP BREATHING!"

Yeah. Drop dead, mom!

I am happy to say that Cindy did not lose her life that day. Her precious grandbaby was born, and as soon as Karen was holding her baby, the first thing she said was, "Mom, get over here and see this sweet girl!"

Mothers and daughters... such a complicated, beautiful relationship!

CHAPTER 16

sisters

---

*W*HAT ABOUT SISTERS ATTENDING a birth? I
remember both of my sisters very well in
each of my births they attended. **They actually
represent the two qualities that I believe to be the
most helpful for a mom during labor: nurture and
empowerment.** My baby sister, Amelia, is
definitely the comforter and provides so much
support through nurturing. Every birthing mom
needs to feel taken care of. My other sister,
Maranatha, (who acts the part of the oldest, even
though I was born first) brings me so much strength
and confidence. Her ability to empower me to do
the job at hand is extremely valuable. This
combination is so effective, I have dedicated an
entire section of my doula training to explaining

how this works. Here are some examples of my sisters in action.

We will start with Amelia JoAnn, or sweet Meena Jo as we liked to call her. Amelia is the sister you would find laying down with me on my bed during labor. She would speak softly and ask if I needed a drink or a cool cloth. She told me frequently how beautiful I was and fed me my dinner after birth. She held my hair back while I threw-up and literally held me up while I pushed out my third child. Amelia even shaved my legs while I was sitting on the potty. Only a sister would do that.

Maranatha, on the other hand, would be the one walking around the block with me telling me to keep a fast pace so that baby would get here sooner. Maranatha would coach me with phrases like, "You can do this, Micah!" "Come-on, you're strong enough!" "You're doin' it. I can see that baby. Don't give up!" "YES MICAH! That's it!" She was the one paying attention to my mental and emotional well-being. She could read me like no other. She would counsel my husband and enlighten my midwife on what would work best for me. When I expressed doubt, she would affirm.

Now, put the two together and you get perfect support! You also get two people that know all of your secrets and inside jokes. I am the entertainer of the three of us, and, for some reason, they thought I still needed to be even while having a baby.

"Hey, Micah, look over here at the video camera and say 'Hiiii everybody!' Now smile, Micah."

"I'm busy right now, girls."

Of course, this only entertained my sisters that much more and laughter erupted.

"Micah, show everybody how you can pop your jaw and your creepy missing earlobe."

Are you serious?

"Hey, Micah, do the imitation of that Muppet character when she says, 'Look, mom, if I want to walk on the beach naked, it's my life, okaaay'. Y'all, this is so funny, watch!"

Who invited y'all?

"Micah, we just thought of the perfect

costume for you to wear at the party. You can go as a chicken who laid an egg! Get it, the baby is the egg!"

My sisters erupted in laughter. *This cannot be happening.*

"Look, you guys. Micah's doin' that dance move where you shift your hips side to side and gradually slide down to the ground. You go, girl!"

I am a great dancer but COME ON!

It's called swaying and squatting, and it's not sexy!

"Y'all have had enough fun for one day. Time to zip it. In fact, go get me a mango smoothie and make it spiked."

If you have sisters then you are probably laughing and commiserating with me. Like I said before, you get the good with the bad. Our sisters are for us, but at times they also compete against us.

There have been several times when a client's sister will come up to me and whisper, "I'm just not sure she can do this." or "Micah, what are you really thinking? Does my sis have what it takes?"

Of course, I reassure them that their sister is killing it!

I had one client who invited both of her sisters to her birth. One of them had a natural childbirth and had encouraged my client in this direction. The other sister went the epidural route and was not discrete at all with her doubts.

"Patricia, you're crazy. I don't know why you're doing this without drugs."

This was Kendra's first phrase out of her mouth when she entered the hospital room. Patricia's other sister, Felicia, had not arrived yet. Patricia did not respond to this comment, and I kept my mouth shut... for now.

After three to four hours of textbook laboring, Felicia finally arrived with her baby in tow.

"I'm here! How are you doing, Patricia?"

"I'm feelin' good, but it's getting more intense!"

"Well, you've got this. I remember when it got more intense for me. You'll be fine. Piece of cake."

"Why are you encouraging this, Felicia? She's clearly hurting! This is so stupid! Just take the drugs already!"

"Shut up, Kendra! Not everyone is afraid of a little pain."

Oh snap! She did NOT! (snap, snap)

"Kendra, I need you to be more supportive of my choice to do this naturally. If you can't then..."

"I'm just sayin that I know you can't do this. You got an epidural with the first two, and I don't why this will be any different."

"Because she wants it to be different, you Bii... rrraat!"

No, you were right the first time.

I shifted the tone by focusing on Patricia by using some misdirection.

"Okay, girl. Let's shake it up a little. How about you and hubby walk the halls for about thirty minutes? Sound good?"

If she started thinking about her birth, she would stop thinking about her "bii...rrraatty" sister.

"Sounds great!"

Yep, my clients believe that I am a magician.

Kendra took the bait and announced that she was going to grab a snack and would be back soon. It was time to check in with my client.

"Patricia? Are you okay? You need to let me know if all this interaction is going to be a distraction for you."

"I will. I just want both my sisters to see that I can do it!"

"You absolutely can do it! Just remember that the goal is a positive birth experience, whatever that ends up looking like. I have all the confidence in the world that you're strong enough. No doubt! Let's just focus on what we can control right now and let it all play out. Deal?"

"Deal."

Smiles returned and Patricia headed out for her walk.

Fast forward. It had been about sixteen hours of laboring and Patricia was still only five centimeters dilated. The contractions had been right on top of each other for about an hour. This is usually a clue that Baby is probably "sunny-side-up" and is having a hard time turning. Patricia was already on Pitocin and in tears. This is a miserable place for a mom to be, and I would not ask or expect anyone to do something I could not do. **I AM NOT INTO TORTURE!**

Patricia's doctor walked in. "How are you holding up, Patricia?"

"Not gonna lie, I'm struggling."

I can hear whispers behind me. "Of course, she's struggling. If I couldn't do it, she can't do it. Freakin' crazy!"

Jealous much?

"Let's check you and see if we've progressed any in the last couple of hours."

Nope.

Position is EVERYTHING, y'all!

"Okay, you're still a five and Baby is posterior. I think we need to turn up the Pitocin."

"WHAT?! NO WAY!"

This is a natural response. I was with her on this one but offered some additional explanation.

"Here's the thing. We've gotta get some stronger contractions to get Baby to turn. Otherwise, you're gonna keep laboring with no progress. That's not what you want. I know this is hard to hear. Tell me what you're thinking so I can help you process."

"I'm just spent, and I can't imagine it getting harder. I want the epidural. I'm done. Is that okay, Micah? What do you think?"

"Girl! You know I'm not into torture! Looks like your body needs a little help, and there's nothing wrong with that. I know that if Baby would have been lined up then you could have done it without the drugs, no problem! Let's get you some relief and some rest. You need to recover and get some more energy because you still have a baby to push out."

Patricia started to cry and reached for my hand.

"Thank you, Micah. Thank you for understanding. I feel so much better about my choice now. I want the epidural please."

The doctor informed everyone that only the nurse and I could be in there for the epidural procedure. Patricia's sisters left, and on their way out, they stopped by her bed for a few last words.

Felicia spoke up first. "We'll be right back. It's gonna be okay."

"I told you. I knew you couldn't do it."

If you don't smack her, I might.

Patricia sat up straight with a determined look on her face.

"Get your negative ass out of my room, and I'll call you once we get home. I'm not gonna let you make me feel like a failure just because I am in need.

You need an attitude check and some time in prayer before contacting me." *Sayonara.*

That is not weakness, y'all, that is one strong Mother Hubbard setting her boundaries and taking care of what she needs. **Somehow, birth turns you into Superwoman no matter what path you take!**

My client Lacey had her sister attending for a specific role. She was going to be the videographer during the birth. This was a relatively new assignment for Lilly, but she was up for the challenge. Lilly is an artist, the creative type, and she actually did a great job getting shots that most birth photographers cannot. You see, you have to be a photo-ninja at a birth. The laboring mom needs to be oblivious to your presence. You do not want to be a distraction, but you have to capture the moments that every mama wants.

However, because Lilly was her sister, there was free reign to move about the cabin. Lilly got right to work as if she had entered TIME's Top 100 Photo contest. Lilly was everywhere! She followed us on our walk in the halls; she would get in her sister's face, then sway the camera back and forth to our rhythm. She would frequently say, "Okay, stop and look over here." or "Wait, back that up and do it again." (This is a BIG no-no in the birth photography world). Lilly even stood up on top of the bathtub, while her sister was in it, to get an aerial view. *Hilarious.*

It was time to start pushing, and Lilly began looking for the perfect spot to set up. She discovered the location, then proceeded to unlock the wheels on the bed in order to move it away from the wall. She wanted to stand behind the head of the bed to capture the moment Baby was born. *She's actually after the Pulitzer Prize.*

Once everyone was in their spot, and we could see Baby's head, the delivery process began. The nurses and I were coaching my client as she started to push her baby out.

"MMMMMMMM. OOOOOOOH."

"Whoa. Okay. Hang on. UUUUUMMMMM!"

Who's this coming from? It was not my client. She was only grunting a little.

"I'm not okay! I'm not okay!"

Who's not okay?

Well, that became painfully obvious in a matter of seconds.

CRASH!

Lilly dropped the camera then stumbled over the chords connected to her sister. She pushed the nurses tending to her sister out of the way and collapsed in her mom's arms.

"It's just too much for me! I can't mom, I just can't!"

Homegirl. You did NOT just say that out loud!

"HUUUUUUUAAAAAAAAAAAH! GET HER OUT!"

"One more good push, and she's here!"

Lilly left the room.

So much for capturing the "very specific, special, never gettin' that back again" moment.

"HAAAAAAAAAAAUUUUUUUUUAAAAH! Oh my gosh! My baby! Where is she?"

"She's right here! You did it!"

"No, where's Lilly?"

Is that where your head's at?

Lacey's mom jumped in. "Oh honey, you know how sensitive your sister is. It was just too emotional and too hard for her. She stepped outside for a minute. I'm sure she'll be fine."

Well, bless her heart!

Y'all feelin' me? Lacey sure was!

"I'm sure she WON'T be fine 'cause she's gonna get an earful! Too emotional?! Too hard?! I can't believe she left! What the hell?"

"Oh Lacey, this is her texting me on my phone. Let me see. She says that she's okay and that..."

"UMMM. No thanks. I don't need to hear what she has to say. Tell her to go on home and recover, and that I'm fine... thanks for asking. Prima Donna."

That was quite the performance. I'll give her that.

One last story. My client, Ashlin, and her husband, Eli, were actually good friends of our family. I was super excited about attending their birth. Ashlin's labor was long, but she was absolutely brilliant. What a Rock Star! After many hours of laboring, it was finally time for her to push. "Ashlin, I'm so proud of you, girl! You've got this!"

"Thanks, Micah, I'm so ready to meet our little girl. Is there something else I need to be doing?"

"Nope. Just keep starting with a good deep breath then trap all of that power, bear down, and focus all of that strength in your bottom. Don't let the power out of your mouth. Make sense?"

"Yep. I got it."

Now, Ashlin had invited her mom and sister to attend, and, while her mom was standing off behind a nurse, her sister was ALL IN! Ashlin's sister, Louisa, was right beside her holding her hand. At some point, I began to notice that she was getting into Ashlin's rhythm of breathing and holding her own breath. That's pretty normal. What happened next is not so normal.

I continued to coach Ashlin. "Okay Ashlin, here we go. Fill your lungs, trap that power, and push!"

"AAAAAAAAAAAAAAAAAAAH!!!!!"

Wait what?

I looked at Ashlin and her eyes and mouth were closed. She took another deep breath.

"AAAAAAAAAUUUUUUUUAAAAAA!!"

It was not Ashlin. It was Louisa! I was stunned.

"AAAAAAAAAAAAAAAAAAAAAAAH!!!"

The contraction ended, and I looked over at Louisa to see what had possibly possessed her. Louisa looked at Ashlin with utter excitement!

"Oh my gosh, Ashlin! That was so great! Let's do it again."

I was not sure Louisa understood the concept of what we were doing there. *No time for conversation, here comes another one.*

"AAAAAAAAAUUUUUAAAAAH!!"

Okay that's it. Cut!

I was so distracted by this person who was screaming like SHE was having the baby... scratch that, like a chick in a horror film. Yes, blood curdling screams. *People!* I tried to redirect the attention to my client.

"Ashlin, you've gotta push all in your bottom and not in your face. Remember, trap that power. Don't let it out of your mouth."

"HUUUUUUAAAAAAAAAAUUUUUH!"

Louisa did not take the hint. She was panting like a dog right in her sister's face. I am sure this is already obvious, but Louisa had not experienced birth for herself yet. I was trying to gather myself and just focus on the true laboring mama in the room.

"You're doing so good, girl. This baby is gonna be here in no time. How's all this workin' for ya?"

...Including the screaming banshee?

"I think it's good. Am I pushing in the right place?"

The midwife finally spoke up. "You are absolutely pushing in the right spot, and Baby is moving down nicely. We just want to all remember that we're supporting Ashlin, so that she can focus on controlled breathing and pushing."

There you go. Take control of this room and any crazy sisters.

Louisa responded. "That's right! Let's do this! You ready, sis!"

Louisa was so jacked up with energy.

Cue contraction.

"Deep breath, Ashlin, and push, girl."

"BLAAAAAAAAAH!! AAAAAAAAAH!!"

Y'all, I just can't with this one anymore.

The midwife instructed again. "She's comin' Ashlin. Just give me a really good, focused push, then stop so we can let Baby's head stretch your skin a little."

Louisa was right on cue.

"HERRRRRRRAAAAAAUUUAAAAAAH!!"

"That's it, Ashlin. Baby is right here. Take a breath for a second and try not to push."

"Ooooooo, that hurts. Can I push now?"

"I've got this, sis."

"HHHUUUAAAAAAAAAAAAAAAAAAH!"

"NO! Stop pushing."

Now the midwife was confused. Ashlin was not pushing, that was Louisa who had apparently taken control of her sister's body.

Louisa was huffing and puffing and managed to say, "Oh my gosh. I'm so sorry. I forgot you said not to push. My bad."

Inconceivable!

"This is helping you right, Ash? Cause I just can't stop!"

"It actually is helping 'cause I am completely out of energy. Just take over, Lou."

Kind of thought she had.

You know what, y'all, whatever works. **I do not fix or tweak or change what is working for a mama.**

Soooooo, am I coaching Louisa now? Whatever.

The midwife actually got on board as well.

"Okay ladies, here we go. Last big push!"

You know the end. Louisa gave it all she had with her loudest yelp and holler, then out popped baby... from Ashlin's vagina.

Gotta love the sister's bond.

CHAPTER 17

coaches' award

I HAVE ONLY HAD a couple of births where a client was considering having one of her children at the birth. One client did not have much of a choice. The birth was going fast, so she had to bring her toddler with her.

However, my client, Dana, and her husband, Doyle, were very excited about the idea of their eight-year-old son being there. We had many conversations while she was pregnant about him attending, and their son's desire was evident as well. I felt quite confident in this couple. They are both super smart, self-proclaimed science nerds and the little they had told me about their son gave me the impression that he was probably smarter than me. My only counsel in all of it was to have a

"Plan B" just in case Jimmy became unsure, uncomfortable, or scared. You never know how a child will respond to any circumstance, much less a birth. They agreed to have a loved one in the waiting room as a precaution for Jimmy.

It was Game Day, and Dana was super excited but also anxious. She was attempting a VBAC with this birth. Baby's heart rate was being monitored but that did not stop us from being active. Her labor was wonderful, and we were getting closer to transition. Baby was turned a little funny, and we were doing some lunges to help open up her pelvis so Baby could wiggle down.

Throughout labor, Jimmy did great. He was not too focused on us because it was pretty uneventful, although he would occasionally ask a highly intelligent question.

"Dad? I see how the monitor is picking up Josiah's heart rate, but what is that second monitor for?"

"That is measuring mom's contractions. They want to make sure that when mom is having a contraction, Josiah's heart rate is a reflection of that.

They also want to make sure the contractions are strong enough and are doing their job effectively."

"Well, all you have to do is look at mom for that."

THANK YOU, Jimmy! Even an eight-year-old gets it.

"What's transition?"

"It's just like it sounds. Mom is transitioning from labor to delivery. This means that her body is just about ready to push your baby brother out."

"It's about time. Let's do this, mom!"

Jimmy was a complete delight! He brought so much joy and positive energy to the room and, quite frankly, to his mom.

"Did you hear that, Dana? Big Brother is ready to go."

"I am too little man… trust me."

Once Dana made it through transition, my coaching increased.

"Okay, girl, it's time to shift gears. The goal during labor is to relax and allow the contractions to do their job. You are just breathing through them and giving into the process. That time is over. Now it's time to do something about what you're experiencing. You feel pressure in your bottom, go towards that pressure. If it hurts, you push it all down and out of your bottom. Make sense?"

"Yes ma'am."

Remember, "ma'am" does not mean I am old; it means she is a Texan.

"When you feel that contraction coming on, fill your lungs and bear down."

Dana drew a deep breath and so did Jimmy.

"Now trap all that power and go towards the pressure."

"Go towards it, mom."

"That was perfect, Dana. Do that again."

"Did you hear that? It was perfect, mom!"

"HMMMMMMMM! HMMMOOOOOAH!"

"That was it! Great job, Dana."

"That was it, mom!"

Jimmy was now on his feet and pacing the floor. He was ALL IN! Y'all, he was such a blast.

"Okay, y'all, here comes another one. HAAAAAAAAAAAAAAAAAAAAAAH!"

"That's it. Another deep breath and go right back to where you were. Go towards the pressure."

"Go towards it, mom!"

"HMMMMMMMMMMMMMMMM! THIS IS SOOO HAAARD! HMMMAAAAOOH!

"I know it, girl. But you are making so much headway. Baby is comin' down. Keep doin' what you're doing."

That contraction ended, and Jimmy started talking to himself while pacing the floor.

"We KNOW it's hard, but there IS progress. Gotta keep doin' what you're doin'. Josiah is comin' down, and I'm gonna get to see him. MOM! I'm about to see my baby brother!"

Well, that was all it took. I have never said anything to a mom quite that motivating. Dana smiled, tears moistened her eyes, and she sat up a little straighter. *Alright Jimmy, what's next?!*

Another contraction began as one of the nurses was stretching her perineum. Now, when a nurse says, "that's it, right there," then you know your client is pushing in the right spot. **Remember, magic happens when you push in the Sweet Spot.**

"That's it, Dana. Right there where my fingers are."

"This is the one, girl! Push right there!"

"This is the one, mom!"

"AHHHHHHHHH!"

The contraction ended, and the nurse asked Dana if she could feel the difference in that push. Dana shook her head yes and closed her eyes to catch her breath. *Never mind. Here comes another.*

"HUUUUUUUAAAAAAAAAAAAH!"

"Right there, Dana, right where my fingers are. Yes! Push!"

"Come on, girl. This is the one! Don't let go of this one!"

"Mom! Don't let go of this one! Don't let go of this one! Don't let go!"

"MMUUUUUUUUUAAAAAAAAAA!"

"YES, MOM, YES! That's the one!"

"Baby's head is crowning. Dana, stop pushing and breath."

The nurse wanted Dana to slow down for two reasons: one, she wanted to give the head time to stretch her perineum, and two, she had not called the doctor yet. *Whoops!*

"I CAAAN'T STOP!"

"We're NOT gonna stop! We're goin'! You got this, mama!"

Dana's contraction ended, so she rested before the next one. You only want a mama pushing with the contraction.

I tried to get Dana's attention. "Hey, girl. Look at me for a sec. You're doin' it. You're almost done. We need you to hold on just for a minute. We want Baby to help stretch you out, so you don't tear. Can you hear me?"

"Mama? What's wrong with her ears? Why can't she hear?"

Doyle addressed this question. "Hey, son, great question. Nothing is wrong with her ears. You know when we are trying to get your attention for some kind of instruction and we say, 'Are your ears on?' ...same thing."

"OOOH! Mama, put your ears on. We're trying to talk to you. Can you hear me? I want to tell you that I love you, and I KNOW you can do this!"

"Thank you, son. I'm ready. Are you ready?"

They should have just hired Jimmy.

"I AM SOOO READY! Let's go, you guys!"

Right on cue, another contraction began. Dana got one deep breath, started to push, and *voila*, out popped a head!

"OH MY GOSH! DAD! Are you seein' this? It's like an alien!"

The room erupted with laughter as Baby came flying out!

Jimmy started jumping up and down. "WE DID IT! MOM! WE DID IT, WE DID IT!"

"We sure did, buddy! Oh my gosh, I HAD A VBAC! I can't believe it! I'm so glad you were here, Jimmy! Want to meet your brother?"

"WOO-HOO! Yes ma'am!"

The nurse put the squalling baby on Dana, and Jimmy walked over to his mom.

"Hey, little bro. I'm here. It's okay. It's okay, Josiah. It's all over now, Jo Jo."

Jimmy patted Josiah's head like a puppy, and within two seconds, that baby stopped crying.

"You're okay, boy. That's it, Jo Jo. I'm gonna call him 'Jo Jo.'"

Dana smiled at her son who had coached her to the very end, then looked down at Josiah.

"Hey, Jo Jo. Want to meet your big brother, Jimmy?"

That baby lifted his head up and locked eyes with his role model, superhero, best friend, and big brother, Jimmy.

And the Coaches' Award goes to... you guessed it.

That is what every experience should be like when a loved one is in the room. You have to have people in your corner cheering you on. As a laboring mom, you thrive when others recognize and affirm your efforts. First of all, you no longer have to doubt if you are doing it "right." There are people watching you and telling you, "Great Job." That is a big one for mamas. Second, our loved ones know us well. They are already in our lives, and we share more than just this birthing moment together. **Remember that normalcy is your friend, and other people in the room can bring that with them.** Lastly, who doesn't like being celebrated? Hearing praise and encouragement, excitement, and joy, gives you strength as you bring your little one into the world. Birth is amazing and hard, and every woman needs their due credit. You earned it, girlfriend, now take a nap.

CHAPTER 18

you want me to do WHAT?

*A*S A DOULA, I can get some pretty unique and, at times, funny requests. Now, I am not just talking about the occasional request of absolutely no talking (hard to coach with that approach), "do not touch me," or it being pitch black in the room. I am not even referring to my very picky clients that have the temperature adjusted every two minutes. Fifty degrees frozen tundra one minute to the heater on full blast the next. I am referring to things that no one else had ever asked me before or probably will never ask me again.

Very early on in my training, I was attending a home birth. The midwife had just called me to head over to their home. Everyone was in the bedroom, and it was extremely peaceful. I observed the mom for a few contractions so I could get a feel for how she was managing labor. It was pretty textbook as far as I was concerned. About an hour went by and I was intermittently affirming her. I noticed she was starting to lose the rhythm that had worked for her for so long. It was apparent that she was fully into active labor and possibly headed into transition.

"Leah, you're doing great! I know it's starting to get harder, but you're managing your contractions perfectly."

Now Leah had not spoken a word throughout her labor. It is very unusual to not even communicate between contractions, but it was working for her. **I do not meddle with a mama's successful ritual.**

A very strong contraction hit Leah, and she began moaning through it.

"That's it, Leah. Perfect. I know it's getting harder and more painful, but you've got this."

The contraction ended and she went back to resting between the contractions.

"Leah, I'm so proud of you! Try not to focus

on the pain, and just keep breathing through the contractions. Don't change a thing."

No response.

Is this helpful at all? I just can't read her.

All I had to go on was the fact that she was so calm. *I'm gonna assume it's workin'.*

A minute later, another strong contraction began.

"Get a good deep breath in through your nose, then blow all the pain down and out through your bottom."

Leah followed the instructions and continued to breathe perfectly through the contraction. When that contraction ended, the midwife quietly motioned for me to follow her out of the room.

"Hey, what's up?"

"Okay, Micah. I know you didn't know this, but I've got to tell you because it is a specific request from Leah about her birth."

"Okay great. What is it?"

"She doesn't want anyone to say the word 'pain.'"

UHHHHH. That would have been helpful an hour

ago. YIKES! I felt like a complete failure and like I was being super insensitive. *Now what?*

"Oh no! I think I've said that maybe twenty times. I feel terrible!"

"Don't worry about it at all. Your coaching is fabulous! Seriously, keep doing what you're doing. Just don't use the word 'pain.'"

Yep. Caught that. Let's do this.

As we walked back into the room, we got settled in time for another contraction.

"Alright, Leah. So... good." For the moment, that word was all I could come up with.

Well, that's not gonna work. Come on Micah, you got this. Just keep doin' what you're doin'. I was now coaching myself.

The contraction ended.

"That was fantastic, Leah. You are absolutely killin' it!"

Oops. Can I say "killin'?"

Another contraction began.

"Here we go, Leah, fill those lungs, then blow all the paaa...rrressure down and out."

Oh, good grief.

Now, Leah had raised her volume quite a bit to more than just a low moan.

"MMMMMMOOOOOOOOOAAAAAAAH! AAAAAAAAAAAAAAH!"

"That's it, girl. This is a hard one, and it's a paaaaii... a good one."

Did I catch it in time? This may be my demise. Have this baby already!

Thankfully, the midwife announced that the head was crowning.

"Here we go, Leah! Final pushes up ahead. Get a deep breath, and push all the paaa... I mean, PUSH!"

In just two pushes, Baby was born! *Thank goodness. I sucked at that!* I wondered what Leah was thinking, or if she was going to say anything about me breaking her one and only rule.

"Congratulations, Leah! You were phenomenal!"

"Oh, thank you, Micah. So were you! I just kept focusing on what you were saying. It helped so much!"

Are you talkin' to me?

I was dumbfounded. "Well, it was my absolute pleasure! Really, you were so calm and so peaceful. Such a great birth!"

"Awwww! Thanks. I just knew that I was gonna have to stay calm in order to stay focused. 'Cause once I get excited or anxious, it's OVER."

Let me leave you with two things about this birth. One, I trained myself to never use the word pain again; I learned a valuable lesson. **Women do not need to be reminded they are in pain. If you say it, they are going to think about it and focus on the very thing you do not want them to focus on.** So, thank you for that, Leah. Second, once Leah broke her silence, she jabbered nonstop for two hours. I have NEVER seen anyone talk that much. Birth is funny, y'all.

I had another client whose request was not funny, but trying to meet this request was. This client was extremely modest. Most women who start off that way do not end that way. As labor goes on, they do not care anymore about who sees what. This mama was different. She told me how important it was for her to stay covered.

Well into the birth, I could see that she was very serious about this! She kept her bra and t-shirt on the whole time, but she got tired of removing her pants over and over. This client was a mover, and she primarily walked and swayed. I took one of the blankets and wrapped it around her like a toga. Keeping that toga in place while she was walking was pretty comical. It kept slipping, and I looked like the mother of the bride fussing over her daughter's train. She was walking like a penguin, which meant in order for me to keep the same stride, so was I.

"I'm your Huckleberry."

Another unusual scenario involved my client's husband. Because of Ned's line of work, the couple wanted to protect their identity. If anyone were to ask for them, the nurses were coached to say, "That's not a name I recognize, and I cannot let you come back." The truth is, no one should have been asking to see them because they did not tell anyone they were even at the hospital. The strange part was that we were all instructed to call them phony names, even while in their private room with no one else but us. That was a new one. *I'll do my best, Bonnie and Clyde, Sonny and Cher, Romeo and Juliet.*

I have also had my fair share of requests that were quite personal. Juliet had just given birth to her baby boy and was beginning to try breastfeeding. Like most newborns, he was struggling a little with his latch. We focused on the typical contributing factors with latching correctly. For about half an hour, she got his body lined up, his nose pointed at the nipple, and waited for him to have a wide-open mouth. It was not working. I decided mom and baby should take a break for a bit. **You do not want to inadvertently train your newborn to be frustrated at the breast.** Finding another way to comfort your baby so they can calm down will help when you decide it is time to try again.

After another half hour went by, she tried again. She switched sides, dried her nipples off, and even stimulated them to help firm them up. He just kept slipping off. We finally asked for a breast pump so that she could get a little colostrum going and help shape her nipples out a bit more. That did not work either. By now, Baby was frustrated, and Juliet was emotional.

"Micah, what's wrong with me?"

"Nothing is wrong with you. This can just take some time. It's a process and a combination of his latch and your anatomy. Your nipples just aren't protruding at all. They're pretty flat. But the more you breastfeed, pump, and stimulate them, the firmer they'll get. Make sense?"

"Yes. That makes sense. I just don't want to starve my baby!"

Cue the tears. *Sweet mama.*

"Juliet, we are a long way from that. However, I do understand what you're feeling. Don't give up. It's gonna happen."

After a few little sniffles, Juliet looked at me with big pleading blue eyes just like Puss in Boots in the movie *Shrek II.*

"Micah, will you rub ice on my nipples and make them hard?"

Come Again?

If she was not already so pitifully forlorn, I would have busted out with an uncontrollable belly laugh and a hard "NO."

The humor in birth, y'all, is a real thing! I am going to leave you in suspense on whether I accommodated her or not.

Here is another one. Ginger was a repeat client and was rocking labor, "doin' her thang". She was complete and it was time to start pushing. Ginger had one major issue though, hemorrhoids! Now, this is the Devil's Curse on these poor mamas. It is not uncommon, though, for a pregnant woman to have them. You always hope that it gets better before childbirth, this was not the case for Ginger.

"Oh, you guys, I do not want to push! I'm so scared 'cause I know it's gonna hurt with these hemorrhoids!"

That's an understatement, poor thing.

The midwife, Judy responded. "Ginger. There's just not a whole lot we can do for that, unfortunately. I will do my best to help alleviate as much discomfort as I can."

Another contraction came and she tried to push.

"HMMMMMM! OUCH! HMMMMMMM! OH NO! I can't do that again!"

Judy had a suggestion. "Ginger, do you want to try and hold your hemorrhoids in place during this next push?

That's not a suggestion, Judy, that's just plain ridiculous!

"I guess so. Can you place my finger on the right spot?"

The midwife tried to put her hand where she could reach.

Here goes nothin'.

"HMMMMMMM! OUCHY!"

"Whatcha think about that?"

As if I need to ask.

"I thought it might help but I just couldn't keep the right amount of pressure while I was pushing."

"Got it. That makes sense. I wonder if there's anything else, Judy?"

"It seems like that might work, but I'm not sure if I can catch a baby and hold that hemorrhoid."

"Micah?"

"Yes, Ginger?"

"Will you please hold my hemorrhoids in place?"

Judy smirked. What came out of my mouth was not what I thought I would have said to this question.

"You bet!"

Wait, what?! I meant, "for an extra grand!"

The things I do y'all. I love my clients and would do anything for them! Oh, and keep in mind that Ginger was standing on the floor squatting while pushing. Can you see it? I crawled underneath a woman, giving birth, with my finger essentially up her a**! **The doula business is no joke, yo!**

One of the craziest requests came from Wilma. She and I had been talking about placenta encapsulation throughout her pregnancy; no, that's not the crazy part. She finally hired someone that was going to pick up the placenta from her at the hospital and have it ready for consumption in less than two days. That is a great turn-around.

Here is the rub. The hospital had a policy of holding a placenta for seventy-two hours before releasing it to the mother. Why? I don't have a clue. Needless to say, my client was not happy. Now, that two-day turn-around was going to be five days and all her research said it is better quality within a forty-eight-hour period.

She went round and round with the hospital. Of course, she asked if I could also speak with the people I knew at the hospital. I was willing, but I knew it would not change anything. I helped pursue some different avenues, but it became clear to her that she would have to wait the seventy-two hours.

Fast forward. It was Game Day, and we were at the hospital going on hour ten of labor. It was finally time to push and have this baby, and I could tell she was very distracted. I finally asked her if something was wrong.

"Tell me what's on your mind, Wilma? You seem distracted."

"I'm having a hard time relaxing. I'm just anxious."

"I get that. It's gonna be over soon, and you'll be holding that sweet baby."

Within twenty minutes, Baby was born, and he was a "biggun!" He weighed a whopping ten and a half pounds! Wow! (If you did not know, hospitals do not like big babies. They assume that there is something wrong because "no baby should be that big.")

The nurse immediately took him over to the baby warmer that was right inside the room to do some quick tests. It was now time to deliver the placenta, and Wilma made an announcement.

"Don't forget that I'm keeping my placenta."

"Yep. We're on it."

"I want to see it, though. Can you leave the bucket right there on the table?"

"Sure."

Wilma delivered the placenta and was getting stitched up from her second-degree tear. As soon as the doctor was finished, she stood up to remove all of her disposable gear and throw it away.

Wilma looked at me and said, "Hey, real quick, Micah. Will you steal my placenta?"

What is this - Shawshank Redemption? I'm not doin' time for you!

"You know Ruby, the lady who is doing the encapsulation? She is right outside the entrance of the hospital."

Literally, my jaw dropped, and I just stared at her. I was trying to wrap my head around what she was asking of me.

What? Do you think I am just gonna go into stealth mode and grab this pink bucket without anyone noticing, scoot along the Labor and Delivery halls with this placenta behind my back, then run like heck through the hospital lobby?

After about fifteen seconds of complete silence and shock, I finally blinked and thought carefully of some kind of a reply to give her.

"Hayyylll no!"

I have my limits, y'all.

Finally, this is a story about two clients; two friends actually with the same name and due about a month apart. It was quite confusing because we also had a Lorin due around the same time. My team and I resorted to calling them "Lauren April," "Lauren May," and "the other Lorin."

I was at "Lauren April's" birth who is a first-time mom and going on hour twelve. Labor had been extremely hard. She was stuck at six centimeters and had asked for an epidural. Meanwhile, I get a text from "Lauren May" who is a repeat client.

"Hey, Micah, I know that you are at Lauren's birth, and I hope she is doing well. Just giving you the heads up that I've been having contractions for about five hours now. I'll keep you posted, and tell Lauren I'm thinking about her."

"Got it. Will do."

Hmmmmmmmm? Let's see how this plays out.

About an hour later, I got another text from "Lauren May" saying she was coming to the hospital. "Lauren April" was now all set up with the epidural and was about to get some rest. I decided to let her know what was going on.

"Hey, friend. I'm glad you're feeling better. Let me catch you up a little. Lauren has been texting me, and she is headed to the hospital right now."

"Oh my gosh! She's not due for another three weeks."

"I know right? So, what I'd like to do is when she gets here to check on her real quick, then come back here to you."

"Oh goodness. Nothin goin' on over here. I'm gonna take a nap anyway, so that's great."

I got the text saying that she was in triage and was ten centimeters dilated.

"Gotta go, Lauren. She's here."

"Tell her I said I'll say a little prayer for her."

I rushed out of the door and into the hall. Lauren was on the triage bed being wheeled into her room.

"Hey, girl. You in some kind of a hurry?"

"I can't believe I'm a ten!"

"Well, you're doing great! Keep it up."

The nurse got her into the room and started messing with the monitors. I was sitting on the triage bed beside her when Lauren started pushing.

"HOOOOOOOOH! HUUAAAAAAUUUH!"

"Hey, this baby is comin'!"

The nurse left the room to... *why did she leave the room? Oh dear!*

"HEEE'S COOOMING!"

Yep. He sure was. I could see the head coming out.

"Lauren, reach down and grab your baby!"

"WHAT?! I CAN'T!"

"Yes, you can! Here he comes!"

Lauren reached down and gave another big push.

"HAAAAAAAAAAAAUUUH!"

His head was out! Soon, his body was going to spew out.

Are you kidding me?

"Micah? Help!"

Now y'all already know what I do not do... **I DO NOT leave mamas alone!** I placed my hands, palms up, on the bed right under the baby. As his body was being born, I gently guided him out and helped Lauren get him to her chest.

What's that you say?

My official statement will always be, "**I DON'T DELIVER BABIES!**" However, in the fine print, it might say... "you just call out my name, and you know wherever I am, I'll come runnin'... even to deliver your baby."

Y'all know it all now! Shhhhhhhhh!

the perfect birth story

*I*N MY LIFE, I am pretty proud of a few things: twenty-eight years (and counting) of marriage with my incredible husband; my six children and two grandchildren; my belief that God is bigger and better than what I could ever imagine; and the opportunity and absolute privilege of serving and empowering others as a doula. The stories you just read are obviously more than just stories to me. They represent my journey of growing and becoming a better person because of the amazing people I have encountered. I love what I do!

This book represents me as a doula, a woman who has given birth, and a person trying something new. Writing a book is not something I thought I would have ever accomplished. I have no idea if I will do it again. What I have learned throughout this process is that there are more ways for me to experience, share, and give away what I have to offer others. You just participated in one of them, and I thank you for that. I sincerely hope that by reading this book you gained something. Maybe you were able to remember your own births in a positive light. **Hopefully, you were able to experience joy or even some healing through laughing and recognizing you are not alone.** If so, this book was written for you. Maybe you have never had a baby and the fear of the unknown has caused doubt in your abilities to ever give birth. **Gaining some insight, reading about others, and realizing how normal childbirth is may have encouraged you to look at birth in a different way.** Fabulous! You just made my day!

In my endeavor to write this book, I used humor, tips, and experience to show an aspect of childbirth rarely talked about. It is meant to be enjoyable. I have found my voice in a specific area of life being a doula, and I want to share it with others. **I believe that every woman should feel**

like Superwoman after giving birth. You know, the *snap, snap* "if I can do that, then I can do anything," bad-ass AT-TI-TUDE! Look out world! I am using that mindset and running with it.

I want to leave you with one last birthing experience. My client's name was Aubri, and I attended both of her births. At her first birth, she was thirty-eight weeks pregnant, and her baby was breech. She had tried every natural approach to get this baby to turn but it hadn't. Her doctor had recommended a specific technique called a Cephalic Inversion in order to get the baby's head down. It would have to be done in the hospital, and if it was successful, they would induce Aubri. The doctor did not want the baby to go back to a breech position, so the best option was to go ahead and deliver Baby. Thankfully, it worked! Aubri was admitted to the hospital and was to be induced first thing in the morning.

I arrived around 7 a.m., and Aubri wanted to try some natural options first. *Nipple stimulation it is.* This option would cause the uterus to contract, which was what we wanted. The doctor, nurse, and

I excused ourselves to allow Aubri and her husband, Ollie, some privacy. I grabbed some coffee from the cafeteria and returned about twenty minutes later. I was standing outside the door and heard laughing and talking. I knocked and announced it was me.

"Come in."

"Hey, y'all, how's it comin'?"

The couple looked at each other and began to snicker.

Aubri was blushing. "This isn't gonna work, girl. Ollie couldn't convince his body that this is not AT ALL sexy."

I joined in the laughter and followed up with a question. "So, are we ready to move onto more conventional options?"

"Yep. Bring it on."

The nurse returned to get the Pitocin started, and the doctor came in to break Aubri's water. I am convinced that the nipple stimulation must have worked and "turned on" Aubri's body because three short hours later, a baby was born.

Before sharing her second birth, let me just tell you why this first birth was so important. This woman was faced with a potential C-section because her baby was breech. She had a procedure done that most people would say is painful. Even if the procedure was successful, she was still being induced at thirty-eight weeks. Induction is not always a pleasant route for having a baby because Pitocin produces very intense contractions that are not "wave-like" (starting mild and gradually increasing, then peaking before coming back down). They are immediately strong, lasting at least a minute, with very little resting time between them. *No bueno.* With her only being thirty-eight weeks, she was more susceptible to the procedure failing.

Sometimes, the body just is not ready, and we cannot predict how it will respond to an induction. Aubri wanted to avoid this scenario; however, the natural approach seemed to have failed, and there would be no getting around the interventions and drugs. Pitocin also meant that she would be hooked up to the IV and monitored continuously. Moving around would be more difficult and getting into the tub was no longer an option. This was not the birth she had in mind.

Regardless, Aubri was so thankful that there was another option, and that her baby could be turned and head down. She said the Cephalic Inversion felt like a massage. She quickly wrapped her head around the idea of her body being "forced" to go into labor, and she saw the humor in her and her husband's failed attempts at nipple stimulation. This could have been a very different experience. This birth could have easily been one of the horror stories we hear about where it feels like everything is stacked against you. In this story, Aubri and Ollie remained positive, decided to be engaged in the process, and enjoy their particular birth journey.

Fast forward to Aubri's second birth. This pregnancy was also challenging because of chronic lower back, hip, and pelvic pain she was experiencing. Her water broke around midnight, and she went into labor on her own at thirty-six weeks. She slept for a few hours, then headed to the hospital at five that morning. It was eight hours later before her baby joined us. On paper, this birth also seemed less than perfect. Her chronic pain ended up being very stressful, and she was a little concerned about how birth might make the pain even worse. Having a baby at thirty-six weeks means the baby is premature, and there could be some medical issues to deal with. Being in labor for over twelve hours with your second baby, when you were only in labor for three with your first, could definitely mess with your mind and emotions.

So how did she respond? When she texted me at 1:30 a.m., she said the contractions were getting a little painful, but she was still smiling through them. She commented with enthusiasm that she was able to rest for a couple of hours. Then, she actually said, "Have I told you how incredibly excited I am that this is actually happening, and naturally, to boot?" There was not one mention of being scared or pessimistic about the pain in her tired body.

Once Aubri and Ollie were at the hospital, they played fun music in their room, and yet it was still a peaceful atmosphere. They were both smiling and having a great time. Guess what? Aubri was able to get into the large tub and labor there for several hours. Also, guess what? Ollie was able to get into the large tub with his wife, and the two of them proceeded to tell jokes at how strange this would look to so many people. I think a song came on about sex and the whole scene was just too funny. Everyone in the room (the midwife, her assistant, the nurse, myself, and my apprentice) was laughing, and it honestly felt like a party. We eventually moved her onto the potty (I know, I'm so mean) where the intensity really started to pick up. She was making noises like a woman in transition, and Ollie was sitting right there in front of her.

Watching the two of them, nose to nose, breathing together with her arms wrapped around his head was one of the most moving, satisfying images I have ever seen. Now here is the best part. Aubri started talking about pressure and feeling like she needed to push. We helped her out of the bathroom and walked her towards the bed. She started another contraction, then dropped to her hands and knees on the floor. Four minutes later, she was holding her baby, and I have the best picture I have ever taken of a woman right after she has given birth. The smile, the bliss and the joy were expressed so perfectly on her face. She looked like she had been laughing. Utter delight and even some giggles lasted for probably an hour.

Let me bring this all together and let you in on what I believe. Aubri's first birth, and the way she accepted the hand she was dealt, gave her the tools she needed to create and enjoy her second birth. As great as the first one was, the second one had a feeling that makes birth actually look like what we all romanticize about, but STILL IT WAS NOT PERFECT.

Her circumstances were similar to many others. She remembered and drew strength from the positive outcome of her first birth, in spite of everything thrown at her during her second. She had no reason to believe that this birth could not have the same positive feel. She walked in expecting to enjoy, smile, be lighthearted, and so she set the tone for everyone else. I feel like I am about to start preaching because I feel so passionate about this. **We get to decide our mindset in this process.**

My births were not perfect either, but I can say with confidence, they were excellent. Let me explain further. First of all, you need to know that before the birth of my oldest child, I was labeled as somewhat of a hypochondriac. I was the one who thought every little ache meant something was wrong. I would talk about how bad my paper cut hurt all through dinner. I passed out often and would never willingly go through anything physically challenging. So, I promise you, no one can say my successful births were because I was such a strong person. What changed? For one thing, my husband believed in me and always said I was stronger than I knew.

Now, I was an absolute baby during my pregnancy, in fact, I am the worst pregnant person on earth! Seriously! But once those first contractions started, something clicked. All I needed to do was stay in control of my emotions and decide that I was not going to let my mind go into a downward spiral of panic. I focused on the only thing I could control; relaxing my breathing and allowing the contractions to do their job. Every time a contraction got stronger, I would think, "Yes. This is what I need in order to have this baby." My mind was made up that if I entertained one outrageous thought, I would snap out of my determined trance, hyperventilate, and never return. Apparently, I did this so well that the people in attendance at any of my births were in shock and asked, "How is she doing that?"

They all knew, of course, that my births were not perfect. Like Aubri's, my circumstances were the same as any other woman's. However, when others would tell my birth story, they always included, "Y'all, I've never seen anyone birth as well as Micah. She makes it look so easy."

This is why I said "yes" to helping other women achieve a positive birth experience. As I mentioned earlier, I was not good with pain or physical stress. **Birth is NOT about your physical strength.** This insight was something I could give away to benefit others. Most of what I do in my job is give my clients a different perspective on their current situation. I help redirect them away from what could potentially be negative and ask them to trust me and focus on what is actually in their control. In childbirth, that would be your mind. We honestly cannot control what our bodies are doing, we cannot control how Baby is doing, we cannot control the medical side of things, the list goes on. What we can do is what Aubri did. **We can decide to home in on the absolute miracle of birth, and we can create our own positive, enjoyable atmosphere that anyone would want to bring her baby into.** I have witnessed hundreds of women accomplish this, and like I said, it is something I am very proud to have been a part of.

Acknowledgements

*T*o see this book adventure become a reality has been a joint effort for sure! There are several people I want to thank and acknowledge. First of all, I want to give a shout out to all of my wonderful clients! There are too many to name! Without these women, this book could not exist. I have been absolutely blessed to be in the line of work that I am in. What a privilege to be a part of someone else's monumental events in life. You guys have made my life so much richer, and I care about each and every one of you. More than anything, I hope you guys enjoy this book. It's for you.

Next, I want to acknowledge the most important people in my life, my family! My husband, Michael, has managed the art of completely supporting me while giving me the space to be a thriving individual. Such a gift. He is not only "my person" that brings me stability and strength, but he has been an active part of the book process. From research to proofreading to stylistic editing, this amazing partner has done so much to see this project realized. Thank you, Michael. I love you!

My six children have not only given me my own birth stories to share, they have also brought a tremendous amount of joy, purpose, and growth in my life. I absolutely adore my "Six Roots" - Gabrielle, Jacob, Anna Joy, Isaac, Naomi and Levi!

I want to thank my two sisters, Maranatha and Amelia, for being a part of my birth experiences and allowing me to be a part of theirs. You saw in several chapters how they helped shape my doula career. You guys are a blessing to me! Special shout out to Maranatha for allowing me to attend my first nephew's birth; the first birth I was ever a part of. This is where it all started for me...and I mean ALL! The Introduction will give you a front row seat into how The Humor in Birth was born and why Benjamin Chapman has such a special place in my heart. Luv ya sweet boy (he's 30 now, LOL)!

Thanks to my parents, Keith and Millie Rollins, for never giving up on me and especially during the seasons of life where it appeared as if I had given up on myself. I had no idea I was capable of something like this, but you did! Your encouragement, after only reading a few chapters, to pursue writing this book will forever be appreciated. A very special thanks to my mom for first of all, giving birth to me. It was not the "in vogue" thing to do at the time to have a natural childbirth. I'm sure that hearing your stories made birth a little more real and normal to me. I also love your sense of humor and am grateful to have inherited some of it. This book is the better for it. You inspire me, Millie Ruth! I also want to honor my late father, Stan Owen. You were always thinking outside the box and helped me to do the same. There are so many things that I wish you could have seen and been a part of in my life. I'm confident that you would have been on the front lines, cheering me on, and affirming me tirelessly about writing this book. You would have been proud of this particular accomplishment of mine. Thank you for believing in me. Miss you.

Thank you to my brother and sister-in-law, Andrew and Michéle Owen, for allowing me to be with you in your birth experiences. Your early involvement in my desire to become a doula has been an absolute game-changer for me. I also want to thank Michéle for translating one of my favorite stories in the book into proper Spanish. The story is too funny!

There have been a few people who helped shape and create my passion for supporting women in birth. At the top of the list is Toni Kimpel. Toni was the midwife for three of my home births and she is such a fabulous caregiver! Toni gave me so much of herself; her time and expertise. She allowed me to be a midwife's assistant for her and the experience I gained can never be repaid. I don't think I would be where I am at today without her. Thank you, Toni, for inviting me into the birthing community and pouring into me for those special years!

I've had several friends that allowed me to join in their childbirth experience before I chose the doula profession. Thanks to Sherry Kniffen, Lisa McMann, Kimberly Benevides, Julie Allen, and Laura LeBlanc. Your faith in me to provide support and care for you catapulted me into a job that I love.

I'd also like to acknowledge the Waco birthing community and thank any of you that have helped shape my doula career. From midwives to childbirth educators and other doulas, I have been extremely supported in my area! Thanks to Christy Miller and Kari Herman, midwives who have sent me client after client. They are directly responsible for getting my Waco Doula business up and running! Stephanie Curtice, Rachael Craig and Sondra Johnson were practicing doulas in my area that included me into the birthing community right away. I appreciate you guys. Thanks to Emilie Cunningham who is a childbirth educator in the greater Waco area who became a very impactful colleague, ally, and close friend. You're a gift to Waco! Thanks to all of the OB/GYN's, L&D nurses and midwives who serve Waco, Texas. Your continued support of natural childbirth, the Waco Doula Team and of me is above and beyond!

I now want to take the opportunity to thank Alison Sloan who was my editor. Alison was PERFECT for this project! She's not only a teacher, she has created her own online curriculum for outschool and she is FUNNY. Alison has been my client so she also knows me and my work up close and personal. This was what I would call A God

Thing! You need to know that she worked her little butt off correcting the millions of mistakes that I made. I'm not an avid reader and I NEVER thought I would write a book. I can remember one of the first things she said to me was, "You know that you change tense a lot... like, mid-sentence sometimes?" I said "Okay, I guess that's bad?" You get the picture. My stories would not have been enjoyable to read because I write like I talk. Anyone who picks this book up will be grateful that Alison was on the case.

A few more people who had a direct hand in getting my book published were Maria Heinonen and Michelle Alexander. Maria created the cover of the book and she helped get my social media marketing up and running. That was a challenge! Michelle is my husband's sister and is a writer. She gave great input, proofreading and overview. Grateful to so many who have inspired and encouraged me along the way in my endeavor to write this book.

Lastly, I want to bring honor to the one who has poured more into me than any other. The one who has known me, shaped me, loved me and given me strength every day. My life is meaningless without the one who gave everything so I could live. My Lord and Savior, Jesus Christ, has pursued me and given me hope beyond what I thought possible. He has blessed me with gifts that could only come from Him. I want anything and everything that I touch to bring glory to Him because He deserves all of my praise and all of my heart.

About The Author

Micah Burgess is a certified doula and the owner/founder of Waco Doula in Waco, Texas. She has been supporting women in childbirth for over twenty-five years and, in the last seven years, has mentored several other doulas in her area. Writing this book, starting a blog, and offering doula training are among the new ventures that Micah is adding to career. Micah and her husband, Michael, have six children and two grandchildren. You can follow her journey on Instagram and Facebook @mydoulamicah.

Made in the USA
Monee, IL
14 May 2021